INTERSCIENCE TRACTS ON PHYSICS AND ASTRONOMY
Edited by R. E. MARSHAK
University of Rochester

1. D. J. Hughes

   NEUTRON OPTICS

2. M. S. Livingston

   HIGH-ENERGY ACCELERATORS

3. L. Spitzer, Jr.

   PHYSICS OF FULLY IONIZED GASES

4. T. G. Cowling

   MAGNETOHYDRODYNAMICS

5. D. ter Haar

   INTRODUCTION TO THE PHYSICS OF MANY-BODY SYSTEMS

Additional volumes in preparation

INTRODUCTION TO THE PHYSICS OF MANY-BODY SYSTEMS

D. TER HAAR

The Clarendon Laboratory, Oxford, England

INTERSCIENCE PUBLISHERS, INC., NEW YORK
Interscience Publishers Ltd., London   1958

INTERSCIENCE PUBLISHERS, INC.

250 Fifth Avenue, New York 1, New York

For Great Britain and Northern Ireland:

INTERSCIENCE PUBLISHERS LTD.

88/90 Chancery Lane, London W. C. 2

PRINTED IN THE NETHERLANDS
BY DRUKKERIJ V.H. GEBROEDERS HOITSEMA, GRONINGEN

Preface

As indicated by its title, this book intends to give an introduction to the rapidly growing field of many-body physics. In the restricted space of a tract one can either treat a very limited subject exhaustively or give a survey of a larger field, highlighting the main points, indicating the trend of recent developments, and referring for more detailed discussions to the literature.

This latter approach has been my aim for the present tract. After a short introduction discussing some recent developments in the field and indicating the philosophy behind much of this work, the tract is divided into two unequal parts. The first part deals with theories where one tries to reduce the problem to that of free particles. Chapters 2, 3, and 4 deal very briefly with the self-consistent field method, the statistical theory of the atom, and Brueckner's theory of the nucleus. A slightly more elaborate discussion is given of holes, excitons, and polarons in solid-state physics. The second part begins with a relatively extensive discussion of recent work on collective behaviour theories, and in the last four chapters applications of these theories to different fields are discussed. In keeping with the aim of this tract, references to original papers are rather numerous.

The idea of writing this tract was very much stimulated by discussions at Harwell during the summers of 1956 and 1957, and I should like to express my thanks to Dr. B. H. Flowers for inviting me to his division and to the members and other guests of the Theoretical Division for their discussions.

Oxford,
October 1, 1957.

D. ter Haar

Contents

CHAPTER 1

Introduction

In this introduction we discuss briefly some of the basic ideas of recent developments in the treatment of systems of large numbers of interacting particles.

In discussing the physics of many-body systems it is well to consider briefly theoretical physics in its entirety. We then note that as long as we try to describe physical systems in macroscopic, phenomenological terms, we are often very successful. However, if we try to start from first principles — granting for a moment that we really know what first principles to use — and use a microscopic description we are led to introduce simplifying assumptions at practically every stage. In view of all these simplifications, it is really remarkable how often one is able to obtain results which bear some resemblance to experimentally verifiable facts. The reason is that the treatment of so many systems can be reduced to the treatment of a system of noninteracting (quasi-) particles, and a system of noninteracting particles can be dealt with, using the ordinary methods of statistical mechanics. However, it is well known that as soon as interactions come into play the discussion of the statistical behaviour of a system becomes extremely complicated, even though in using statistical mechanics one has already simplified the problem by considering the average behaviour in the system instead of the detailed behaviour of all the particles. As long as the interactions are so weak that virial expansions can be used and can be cut off after the second virial coefficient, one can still use the formulae of statistical mechanics. In this case only two-body encounters need be considered and those, as is well known, can be reduced to a one-particle problem. As soon as three-particle processes come into play both conceptual difficulties (the admissibility of the assumption of additivity of intermolecular forces) and computational difficulties (nobody has yet attempted to evaluate the quantum-mechanical third virial coefficient, even assuming additivity) loom up. For even higher densities the problems are even more difficult and although a large amount of research has been done in this field (see Yvon 1935, Kirkwood 1946, de Boer 1949, Green 1952, Hirschfelder, Curtiss, and Bird 1954, Brussels 1958)* a lot remains to be done, not the least a clarification of the foundations. If the density is so high that condensation becomes possible, we are nearly completely lost as there seems to be no understanding of the microscopic physical processes responsible for this phase transition, even though the mathematical side was greatly clarified by Yang and Lee (1952). The only liquid which is coming close to being understood is helium II at or near absolute zero through Feynman's work (see Chapter 10). However, its λ-transition, at a finite temperature, is not yet fully understood. The related system of an imperfect Bose-Einstein gas with hard-sphere interactions has also been studied extensively and its properties are slowly being unravelled (Jastrow 1955, Brueckner and Sawada 1957a, b, Huang and Yang 1957, Huang, Yang, and Luttinger 1957, Dyson 1957, Lee, Huang, and Yang 1957).

In the case of solids the situation can often be simplified considerably. For instance, if we may assume the crystal to be perfect and if we may neglect the dispersion of the lattice waves, it is possible to calculate the lattice specific heat and the Debye T^3-law is found which agrees with experimental data at sufficiently low temperatures. Of course, one has thrown overboard a large part of the problem and the work of Born and of Blackman has shown, for

* All references are given at the end of the tract.

instance, how difficult it is to find the exact vibrational spectrum, even if we may assume the crystal to be perfect. Qualitatively one can also understand such problems as transport phenomena in metals, by using the Sommerfeld free-electron theory (Sommerfeld 1928, Sommerfeld and Bethe 1933; see also Wilson 1953). In these cases again the problem is reduced to the consideration of a system of noninteracting particles, phonons for the lattice specific heat, and the charge carriers (fermions with an effective mass not necessarily equal to the electron mass) for transport phenomena.

Finally we want to draw attention to the success of shell models, both in the case of atomic spectra and in the case of nuclear properties. Once again a theory treating the particles (electrons or nucleons) as independent fermions in a common field of force is able to describe the experimental data.

From the above discussion we see that it is apparently often possible to make the reduction to a system of non-interacting particles — or weakly interacting particles — which is necessary in order that the physical properties of the system can be evaluated. Clearly it is of importance to discuss under what circumstances and by what methods this reduction can be achieved. Although the distinction is not by any means clear cut we have for the purposes of the present tract divided the methods used into two groups. The first group is that of the effective field theories, and the second one that of the theories of collective behaviour. In the first part of this tract we discuss the self-consistent field methods, including the Brueckner theory of the nucleus, the statistical theory of the atom, and — not very consistently — the effective mass approximation in solids, excitons, and polarons. The second part is devoted to theories such as the one of Tomonaga (1955a) which give prescriptions for describing collective behaviour of physical systems and also to a discussion of applications of such theories. Before going into a detailed discussion we wish to consider in this introduction the general aspects of the various modes of approach. We shall discuss first of all effective field methods, then the effective mass approach, and finally the introduction of collective coordinates.

The aim of all methods of approach is to obtain a set of coordinates q_j and conjugate momenta p_j such that the Hamiltonian H of the system can be written in the form

$$H = \sum_j H_j(p_j, \ q_j), \tag{1.01}$$

where each term H_j depends on one set of p, q only and where the summation is over all degrees of freedom of the system. The H_j can be written in the form

$$H_j = T_j + U_j, \tag{1.02}$$

where T_j and U_j are respectively the kinetic energy and the potential energy corresponding to the jth degree of freedom. In some cases we should even like to go one step further and find coordinates such that $U_j = 0$ so that we are left with the Hamiltonian of a system of free particles. Of course, this aim is never fully realized, and we will be satisfied if we can obtain a Hamiltonian of the form

$$H = \sum_j H_j(p_j, \ q_j) + H_{\text{int}}, \tag{1.03}$$

where H_{int} cannot be written as a sum of terms depending on only one set of p, q, but where H_{int} is small compared to H_j (at least for most values of the p_j, q_j corresponding to physical situations).

In the self-consistent field theories, one starts from the original Hamiltonian which we shall assume to be of the form

$$H = \sum (\mathbf{p}_j{}^2/2m_j) + \sum U(\mathbf{x}_j) + \tfrac{1}{2} \sum_{j \neq n} U_{jn}(\mathbf{x}_j, \ \mathbf{x}_n), \tag{1.04}$$

where the $\mathbf{x}_j$ are the Cartesian coordinates of the particles in the system, $\mathbf{p}_j$ their momenta, and where the $\sum_{j \neq n}$ includes all the interactions between the particles, which we have assumed to be all two-body interactions. We see that each particle will move in a field which is the sum of the external field $[U(\mathbf{x}_j)]$ and the field produced by all the other particles

$[\sum_{n(\neq j)} U_{jn}]$. The idea now is to smooth out the second part so that the jth particles moves in a potential field depending on $\mathbf{x}_j$ only. If the behaviour of all the particles is known in this effective field, one can check whether that behaviour would lead, indeed, to the assumed smoothed potential. If not, one adjusts the effective field, until the result is self-consistent. This method is rather cumbersome, but it has been applied with success to atoms and recently it has been modified and extended in such a way that it can be applied to nuclei. These applications are discussed in Chapters 2 and 4, respectively. A simplified form of the self-consistent field theory is the statistical model of the atom. Here one treats the electrons as a degenerate Fermi-Dirac gas and adjusts the density in such a way that it is equal to the maximum number of electrons which can be bound within a volume element at a given value of the overall potential. As this potential depends on the electron density, the electron distribution follows in a self-consistent manner. However, the introduction of the idea of a degenerate Fermi-Dirac gas has as a consequence the smoothing out of the overall potential as compared to the Hartree field which shows more clearly the shell structure of the atom. This statistical theory is discussed in Chapter 3.

   We mentioned a moment ago that it is of advantage to obtain a Hamiltonian of the form of equation 1.01, preferably with H_j of the form

$$H_j = \mathbf{p}_j{}^2/2m_j. \qquad (1.05)$$

To some extent it is permissible to treat the system of conduction electrons in a metal or semiconductor using the Hamiltonian of equation 1.01 with H_j given by expression 1.02 where U_j is a periodic potential. It can be shown (see Chapter 5 and Appendix C) that expression 1.02 can be reduced to expression 1.05 in this case, provided m_j is not the mass of a free electron, but a so-called effective mass. This means that we can neglect the interaction between the electron and the periodic potential, provided we replace the electron by a quasi-particle with an effective mass m_j which may under certain circumstances even be negative.

This replacement of a particle of mass m interacting with a field by a free particle of mass m_0, where m_0 is not necessarily equal to m, is a case of mass renormalization. The best-known example of such a renormalization is the case of a free electron where the interaction of the electron with its own electromagnetic field leads to a difference between the "bare" mass and the "experimental" mass. This difference is predicted by the classical electron theory (Lorentz 1909) and was experimentally verified by Lamb and Retherford (1947). Kramers (1938) was the first to introduce renormalization into quantum theory, and since the war an extensive literature has grown up on the subject.

Once we realize the importance of replacing particles interacting with fields by free quasi-particles we also understand the occurrence of polarons which are electrons in polar substances surrounded by a "cloud" of phonons. The interaction is here that of an electron with the polarization field of the medium. Both the effective mass approximation and polarons are discussed in Chapter 5.

In the discussion so far the q_j were coordinates describing the position of a particle or of a quasi-particle which still resembled very closely the "bare" particle it was replacing. However, phonons which we mentioned a moment ago are a typical example of a different kind of quasi-particles which are formed by the collective action of a large number of particles. Quasi-particles very similar to phonons in that they are essentially waves in a solid involving all the particles are spin waves (Bloch 1930; see ter Haar 1957 § 5 for a discussion and further references), magnons (Pomerantschuk 1941a, b, Pomerantschuk and Achieser 1944), and plasmons (see Chapter 8). We refer to review articles by Wonssonski (1952), Pekar (1953), and Bontsch-Brujewitsch (1955) for a discussion of this kind of quasi-particles and especially of the Russian work in this field. For our present discussion it is of importance that it is often possible to find coordinates, ξ_n, which describe collective modes and which are such that the collective part of the Hamiltonian H_c, can be written in the form

$$H_c = \sum_n H_n(\xi_n, \pi_n), \qquad (1.06)$$

where π_n is the momentum conjugate to ξ_n. If H_n is of the form

$$H_n = \tfrac{1}{2} A_n \pi_n^2 + f_n(\xi_n), \qquad (1.07)$$

each collective mode corresponds to a quasi-particle. In many cases H_n will be of the harmonic oscillator type,

$$H_n = \tfrac{1}{2} A_n \pi_n^2 + \tfrac{1}{2} B_n \xi_n^2, \qquad (1.08)$$

and instead of the ξ_n we can use the quanta of this collective mode as our quasi-particles. If equations 1.06 and 1.08 hold exactly, and if the rest of the Hamiltonian is independent of ξ_n, the quanta behave as free particles.

Some authors (notably Yevick and Percus, see Section 6.3) try to find as many ξ_n as there are degrees of freedom so that H_c is identical with the total Hamiltonian. In that case, equation 1.06 will almost always be an approximation. For most systems it is more natural to introduce a number of ξ_n and to describe the other degrees of freedom by as many particle coordinates q_j as are necessary to complete the total number of degrees of freedom. The total Hamiltonian will then be of the form

$$H = \sum_j H_j(p_j, q_j) + \sum_n H_n(\xi_n, \pi_n) + H_{\text{int}}, \qquad (1.09)$$

where H_{int} depends both on the p, q and on the ξ, π. In order that such a separation be successful H_{int} must be small. The only cases where such a separation has been partly successful are liquid helium and the case of nuclei. The difficulty is usually to find the proper q_j.

In Chapter 6 we discuss various methods to introduce collective modes and to find the q_j, and in Chapters 7 to 10 we discuss how these methods can be applied to such problems as liquid helium, nuclei, plasma oscillations, and sound waves.

In conclusion we wish to draw attention to the simplest possible case of a system showing both quasi-particle and collective behaviour. Consider two particles of mass m_1 and m_2 at $\mathbf{x}_1$ and $\mathbf{x}_2$ interacting according to a potential energy $U(\mathbf{x}_1 - \mathbf{x}_2)$ in a homogeneous gravitational field (gravitational acceleration $\mathbf{\acute{g}}$). The Hamiltonian of this system is of the form of equation 1.04 with $U_{12} = U(\mathbf{x}_1 - \mathbf{x}_2)$ and $U(\mathbf{x}) = (\mathbf{\acute{g}} \cdot \mathbf{x})$, or

$$H = (\mathbf{p}_1^2/2m_1) + (\mathbf{p}_2^2/2m_2) + (\mathbf{\acute{g}} \cdot \mathbf{x}_1) + (\mathbf{\acute{g}} \cdot \mathbf{x}_2) + U(\mathbf{x}_1 - \mathbf{x}_2). \tag{1.10}$$

Introducing centre-of-mass coordinates $\mathbf{X}$ and relative coordinates $\mathbf{x}$,

$$M\mathbf{X} = m_1\mathbf{x}_1 + m_2\mathbf{x}_2, \quad M = m_1 + m_2, \quad \mathbf{x} = \mathbf{x}_1 - \mathbf{x}_2, \tag{1.11}$$

and their conjugate momenta $\mathbf{P}$ and $\mathbf{p}$, we get the Hamiltonian

$$H = (\mathbf{P}^2/2M) + (\mathbf{\acute{g}} \cdot \mathbf{X}) + \mathbf{p}^2/2\mu + U(\mathbf{x}), \quad \mu = m_1 m_2/M. \tag{1.12}$$

We see here both the collective behaviour, which is now the motion of the centre of mass, and a quasi-particle of effective mass μ moving in a potential energy field U! This example is not as academic as it might seem as, the electron-hole pairs called excitons (see Section 5.2) are exactly of this type.

PART I

Effective Field Theories

CHAPTER 2

The Hartree-Fock Approximation

In the previous chapter we discussed how one method of attacking the many-body problem lies in finding an effective potential field for each of the particles so that the problem is essentially reduced to a one-particle problem. Since it is known from spectroscopic evidence that the electrons in an atom are moving approximately in single particle orbits, the system of the electrons in an atom should be especially promising for this approach, and Hartree used it for this particular problem. It was found that the same method can also be employed for other problems, for instance, the band theory of solids. There exist excellent accounts of the Hartree method and its extension by Fock (for instance, Hartree 1948, Schiff 1949, Ch. XI, Seitz 1940, Ch. VI, Hund 1956; see also Löwdin 1955a, b, c, 1956) and in the present chapter we shall only briefly discuss the general method. We refer to the articles mentioned above for extensive bibliographies and for a discussion of applications of the method.

Let us consider a system of N particles with a total Hamiltonian given by the equation

$$H = \sum_j H_j + \tfrac{1}{2} \sum_{j \neq n} H_{jn}, \qquad (H_{jn} = H_{nj}) \qquad (2.01)$$

where the first sum is over all particles and the second one over all pairs of particles in the system. The H_j will be the kinetic energy of the jth particle together with the potential energy of that particle in a potential common to all particles ($H_j = T_j + U_j$), which in the case of an atom will be the Coulomb field of the nucleus,

$$H_j = -(\hbar^2/2m)\, \mathbf{\nabla}_j^2 - Ze^2/r_j, \qquad (2.02)$$

where m is the mass of the electron, $-e$ its charge, Ze the charge of the nucleus, which for the sake of simplicity is assumed to be at rest at the origin, and $r_j \; (= |\mathbf{x}_j|)$ the distance of the electron from the origin. The H_{jn} are the interaction potentials which, in the case of an atom, will be of the form

$$H_{jn} = e^2/r_{jn}, \qquad (2.03)$$

where $r_{jn} = |\mathbf{x}_j - \mathbf{x}_n|$. We shall not restrict ourselves to expressions 2.02 and 2.03 in our present discussion.

According to our program we look for eigenfunctions Ψ of H of the form

$$\Psi = \prod_j \psi_j(\mathbf{x}_j), \qquad (2.04)$$

that is, eigenfunctions that are a product of single-particle eigenfunctions. The problem is now to find the ψ_j. For the case of an atom Hartree (1928) suggested that the ψ_j should satisfy a Schrödinger equation where the potential energy was obtained by adding to the Coulomb potential of the nucleus, the Coulomb energy due to the charge distributions of the other electrons; this means that ψ_j must satisfy a Schrödinger equation with a Hamiltonian $H_{(j)}$, given by the expression

$$H_{(j)} = -\frac{\hbar^2}{2m} \, \mathbf{\nabla}_j^{\,2} - \frac{Ze^2}{r_j} + \sum_{n(\neq j)} e^2 \int \frac{|\psi_n(\mathbf{x}_n)|^2}{r_{jn}} \, d^3 \mathbf{x}_n, \quad (2.05)$$

where we have assumed all ψ_j to be normalized, and where here and henceforth $\int \ldots d^3 \mathbf{x}$ indicates an integration over coordinate space.

We shall derive equation 2.05 by requiring that Ψ must satisfy a variational principle (Fock 1930, Slater 1930), that is,

$$\delta \int \Psi^* H \Psi d^{3N} \mathbf{x} = 0, \quad d^{3N} \mathbf{x} = \prod_j d^3 \mathbf{x}_j, \qquad (2.06)$$

with the subsidiary conditions

$$\int |\psi_j|^2 \, d^3 \mathbf{x}_j = 1, \text{ or, } \int (\delta \psi_j^*) \, \psi_j \, d^3 \mathbf{x}_j + \int \psi_j^* \, \delta \psi_j \, d^3 \mathbf{x}_j = 0. \quad (2.07)$$

The variation is here a functional variation, that is, with respect to the ψ_j, and the independent variations are the $2N$ functions $\delta\psi_j$ and $\delta\psi_j^*$. We shall assume that H is Hermitean, and in that case equation 2.06 to which expression 2.07 multiplied by Lagrangian multipliers λ_j is added, can be written in the form

$$\sum_j \int \delta\psi_j^* [H_j + \sum_{n(\neq j)} \int \psi_n^* H_{jn} \psi_n \, d^3 x_n - E_j] \psi_j \, d^3 x_j + \text{C.C.} = 0,$$

$$(2.08)$$

where C.C. stands for the complex conjugate expression, and where E_j is given by the equation

$$-E_j = \sum_{n(\neq j)} \int \psi_n^* H_n \psi_n \, d^3 x_n$$
$$+ \sum_{(j\neq)p\neq n(\neq j)} \int \psi_n^* \psi_p^* H_{np} \psi_n \psi_p \, d^3 x_n \, d^3 x_p + \lambda_j.$$

$$(2.9)$$

As the $\delta\psi_j$ and $\delta\psi_j^*$ are independent, their coefficients must vanish, leading to the equations

$$[H_j + \sum_{n(\neq j)} \int \psi_n^* H_{jn} \psi_n \, d^3 x_n] \psi_j = E_j \psi_j. \quad (2.10)$$

Equations 2.09 and 2.10 form a set of simultaneous differential equations from which the ψ_j can be solved. In practice these equations will usually be solved by successive approximations, that is, one guesses the form of the ψ_j, calculates with those ψ_j the operator on the left-hand side of equation 2.10, and solves the resulting differential equation. The ψ_j obtained in that way are then used to start a new cycle, until a self-consistent set of ψ_j is obtained. It is easily checked that for the case of atoms equation 2.10 corresponds to the Hamiltonian of equation 2.05.

There is one serious objection to the method as we have described it here, namely, that it does not take into account the statistics (or symmetry properties) of the particles. To take care of that Fock generalized the trial wave function in such a way that it possessed from the beginning the necessary symmetry properties. In the case of electrons this means that instead of expression 2.04 one uses for the wave function the expression

$$\Psi' = S_{op}\,\Psi = A \sum_P \varepsilon_P P\Psi, \qquad (2.11)$$

which is a Slater determinant (Slater 1929). In equation
2.11 the summation is over all $N!$ permutations of the
particles, A is a normalizing factor, ε_P is $+1$ for an even and
-1 for an odd permutation, and $P\Psi$ is obtained from Ψ
by permuting the particle coordinates, that is, if the
permutation P of the numbers $1, 2, \ldots, N$ corresponds to
the sequence $k_1, k_2, \ldots, k_N$, $P\Psi$ is given by the equation

$$P\Psi = \psi_1(x_{k_1})\,\psi_2(x_{k_2}) \ldots \psi_N(x_{k_N}). \qquad (2.12)$$

Starting from the trial function of equation 2.11, one
can again obtain differential equations for the ψ_j, which
are now slightly more complicated through the occurrence
of additional terms, the so-called exchange terms.

The use of the properly antisymmetrized wave functions
ensures also that correlation effects are taken into account
to a first approximation. The Coulomb repulsion between
electrons will ensure that two electrons will not get too near
to one another. As far as electrons with parallel spins are
concerned, the antisymmetrization will lead to the same
effect, but the correct correlation between electrons with
antiparallel spins is still lacking. This correlation effect was
studied by Wigner (1934, 1938), and also by Bohm and
Pines (1953, Pines 1953, 1955) in their work on many-
electron systems. It has recently been discussed by Löwdin
(1955c) in his work on an extension of the Hartree-Fock
scheme which among other things can also be applied to
degenerate systems. For Löwdin's work it is important
that S_{op} in equation 2.11 is a so-called projection operator
(von Neumann 1955), that is, that it satisfies the equation
$S^2_{op} = S_{op}$. We must refer to his paper (see also Löwdin
1956) for details.

Before concluding this chapter we want first of all to
mention that Gáspár (1952a, b, 1954) has combined ideas
from the statistical theory of the atom (see next chapter)

with the self-consistent field method and derived a universal function for the self-consistent field.   Secondly, we must mention that the main field of applications of the Hartree-Fock method has been in calculating the one-electron wave function for the electrons in atoms and molecules (for a discussion of these applications see Hartree 1948 and Hund 1956).   Apart from its application to solids the Hartree-Fock method, albeit slightly changed and extended (see Chapter 4) has recently come to the fore in the Brueckner theory of the nucleus.   Thirdly, we must refer to a paper by Kinoshita and Nambu (1954) who have generalized the theory for the case where there is a system of particles interacting through a Bose field.   They introduce two Hartree fields, one for the particles and one for the field quanta. They show that the ordinary Hartree-Fock method, as well as the statistical theory of the atom (see Chapter 3) and Bohm and Pines' plasma theory (see Section 6.4 and Chapter 8) are special cases of their general theory.

Finally we must briefly mention a very successful application of the Hartree-Fock method in solid-state physics, namely, the so-called cellular method (Wigner and Seitz 1933, 1934; see also Seitz 1940, Ch. IX).   In this application, the solid is divided into polyhedra, each centred around an ion, and inside each polyhedron the potential energy is supposed to be spherically symmetric.   The wave function inside each polyhedron is assumed to satisfy the Hartree-Fock equations, and the wave functions in the different polyhedra are joined up in such a way that they and their first derivatives are continuous on the faces of the polyhedra and that the total wave function shows the correct periodic behaviour for the crystal under consideration.   This method has, for instance, been used to calculate the cohesive energy of solids (see, for example, Seitz 1940, Ch. XII).

CHAPTER 3

The Statistical Model of the Atom

Thomas and Fermi introduced statistical considerations into the discussion of electron distributions in heavy atoms. It was found later on that their theory has a wider field of application and can usefully be extended to the discussion of molecules, nuclei, solids, and especially to matter under high pressure. A number of excellent survey articles have recently been published (Gombás 1949, 1956, 1957, March 1957; see also Corson 1951) and we refer to these for extensive bibliographies and for detailed discussions of applications. We shall in this chapter briefly discuss the general ideas of the statistical theory and indicate a few applications.

We mentioned in Chapter I that one way of treating a many-body system is to use statistical methods. The drawback of having to deal with large numbers is turned into an advantage in that way. Although the number of electrons in an atom at first sight does not seem to be sufficiently large to enable us to use statistical methods, it is certainly too large to allow exact solutions of the equations of motion. One way out of this dilemma is the method of the self-consistent fields discussed in the previous chapter, but one is still left with a set of equations which are extremely cumbersome to solve in all practical cases. One is thus driven to try the statistical method. This was done by Thomas (1927) and Fermi (1928) who proceeded as follows:

Let us consider an atom with spherical symmetry corresponding to a potential energy field $U(r)$. Let us now assume that we can divide the space occupied by the

16

atom into cells such that (i) each cell contains a large number of electrons, and (ii) $U(r)$ changes only very slowly in each cell. In that case we can apply statistical methods to each cell. As we are dealing with electrons in quantized orbits, we would expect that we should use quantum statistics, as classical statistics presumably would be a poor approximation. One can, indeed, easily convince oneself that the de Broglie wave length of the electrons will be large compared to (or at least of the same order of magnitude as) the dimensions of the cells, which means that Fermi-Dirac statistics must be used. Moreover, since over practically the whole of the volume of the atom $|U(r)|$ will be large compared to $k_B T$ (k_B Boltzmann's constant and T absolute temperature), as long as $T < 10{,}000°$ K, we can apply the formulae of a completely degenerate Fermi-Dirac system.

Let $n(\mathbf{x})$ be the electron density. The total kinetic energy T of the system is given by the equation

$$T = c_1 \sum n^{5/3} v, \qquad (3.01)$$

where the summation is over all the cells, where v is the cell volume, and where c_1 is given by the equation (compare ter Haar 1954, p. 91)

$$c_1 = \left(\frac{3}{8\pi}\right)^{2/3} \frac{3h^2}{10m}, \qquad (3.02)$$

with m the electron mass. The potential energy consists of two parts, first of all a term U_e which is the interelectronic potential energy,

$$U_e = \frac{e^2}{2} \int \frac{n(\mathbf{x})n(\mathbf{y})}{|\mathbf{x} - \mathbf{y}|} \, d^3\mathbf{x} \, d^3\mathbf{y}, \qquad (3.03)$$

and secondly a term U_n which is the potential energy of the electrons in the electric field of the nucleus (and possibly other external fields) $u(\mathbf{x})$

$$U_n = -e \int u(\mathbf{x})n(\mathbf{x}) \, d^3\mathbf{x}. \qquad (3.04)$$

The total energy E of the system of electrons is given by the expression

$$E = T + U_e + U_n. \tag{3.05}$$

The electron density can be obtained by requiring E to be a minimum under the condition that the total number N of electrons is given,

$$\int n(\mathbf{x})d^3\mathbf{x} = N. \tag{3.06}$$

By the usual variational methods (Frenkel 1928, Lenz 1932) it now follows that

$$n = c_2(U - U_0)^{3/2}, \tag{3.07}$$

where

$$c_2 = (3e/5c_1)^{3/2}, \quad U = u(\mathbf{x}) + v(\mathbf{x}), \tag{3.08}$$

with $v(\mathbf{x})$ the potential due to the electrons,

$$v(\mathbf{x}) = - e \int \frac{n(\mathbf{y})}{|\mathbf{x} - \mathbf{y}|} \, d^3\mathbf{y}. \tag{3.09}$$

In deriving equation 3.07 we have first of all replaced the sum in equation 3.01 by an integral and secondly used the method of Lagrangian multipliers to take the condition given in equation 3.06 into account. The quantity U_0 is the Lagrangian multiplier.

Equation 3.07 gives us one relation between two unknowns, n and U. A second equation follows from Poisson's equation

$$\boldsymbol{\nabla}^2(U - U_0) = 4\pi ne, \tag{3.10}$$

and combining equations 3.07 and 3.10 we get for U the differential equation

$$\boldsymbol{\nabla}^2(U - U_0) = 4\pi c_2 e(U - U_0)^{3/2}, \tag{3.11}$$

which is the basic equation of the Thomas-Fermi theory.

It is of interest to note that Fényes (1948) was able to derive the fundamental equation of the statistical method using the WKB approximation. This shows that the statistical method is essentially semi-classical, and it indicates its limitations.

From equation 3.07 it follows that $U \geqq U_0$, which involves that U_0 is the maximum value of the potential. In the case of an atom the boundary conditions for equation 3.11 are $U - U_0 \to Ze/r$ as $r \to 0$, and $r(U - U_0) \to 0$ as $r \to \infty$ expressing the fact that near the nucleus the nuclear charge determines U and that for sufficiently large r the atom as a whole acts as a neutral body. Introducing dimensionless quantities by the equations

$$U - U_0 = \frac{Ze\chi}{r}, \quad r = \mu t, \quad \mu = (6\pi Z)^{-1/3}\frac{3h^2}{16\pi me^2}, \quad (3.12)$$

and assuming radial symmetry, equation 3.11 can be written in the form

$$t^{1/2}d^2\chi/dt^2 = \chi^{3/2}, \quad \chi \to 1, \quad t \to 0; \quad \chi \to 0, \quad t \to \infty. \quad (3.13)$$

From equation 3.12 we see that there is a scale factor proportional to $Z^{-1/3}$. As at the same time the number of electrons in the case of a neutral atom is equal to Z, we see that our original assumptions will be better warranted for larger values of Z.

We must remark here that the Thomas-Fermi method breaks down either for very small r or for very large r. In the first case because the potential varies too steeply and in the second case because the electron density becomes too small. If exchange effects are taken into account (Dirac 1930) the behaviour at large r is improved, but not at small r.

Apart from including exchange effects, the theory can also be improved and extended in other directions (see Gombás 1957, March 1957, § 9). We may mention a few of them. The first one is an attempt by von Weizsäcker (1935) to take the kinetic energy properly into account. In writing down equation 3.01 we have tacitly assumed all electrons to be free particles, or, in other words, all electron wave functions to be plane waves. One can take the deviation from plane waves into account and the resultant electron densities give a more satisfactory agreement between calculated and experimental data of diamagnetic susceptibilities and atomic energies (see Gombás 1957 and earlier papers by Gombás mentioned there).

Another method to extend the scope of the statistical theory has been by incorporating some results of the self-consistent field method into it. From the self-consistent field work it follows that the idea of electron shells, that is the grouping of the electrons in terms of principal and azimuthal quantum numbers, is a very useful one. This fact led Gombás first of all to take together all the electrons with the same azimuthal quantum number and treat those different groups statistically. This method was extended (Gombás and Ladányi 1955) in the following way to treat the different groups of electrons, characterized by different principal quantum numbers, by the statistical method. First of all Gombás draws attention to the fact that in order to accommodate an extra electron with azimuthal quantum number l at a distance r from the nucleus, one needs at least an energy $- eG_l$, where G_l is given by the equation

$$G_l = - c_3[8\pi^4 r^4 n_l{}^2(2l + 1)^{-2} + r^{-2}], \quad c_3 = e\hbar^2/16\pi^2 m, \quad (3.14)$$

where n_l is the density of electrons of azimuthal quantum number l already present. This additional potential (Zusatzpotential) G_l derives from taking into account the Pauli-principle in each cell in such a way that the electrons in each cell are classified according to l.

The next step is to take into account the principal quantum number n. This is done by building up the atom in stages, each stage corresponding to a different value of n. It is assumed that an electron put into the nth shell will be subject to an additional potential $G_{(n)}$ which is given by the expression

$$G_{(n)} = \sum_{m=1}^{n-1} N_m{}^{-1} \sum_{l=0}^{m-1} n_{(l)}{}^{(m)} G_l{}^{(m)}, \quad (3.15)$$

where N_m is the total number of electrons in the (filled) mth shell, $n_{(l)}^{(m)}$ the number of electrons of azimuthal quantum number l in the mth shell, and $G_l^{(m)}$ as given in expression 3.14, but with n_l the density of electrons of azimuthal quantum number l in the mth shell. This extra potential $G_{(n)}$ is now taken into account in deriving the differential equation for the potential U from a variational principle. The complete procedure is then the following one. First of all the statistical theory is used to find the electron density $n_{(1)}(r)$ in the first shell $(n = 1)$. This density is supposed to satisfy the general equation

$$n_{(m)}(r) = (2\lambda_m)^{2m+1} N_m r^{2m-2} \exp\left[-2\lambda_m r\right]/4\pi(2m)! \quad (3.16)$$

The parameter λ_1 is determined from the variational equations. It is assumed that the electrons with $n > 1$ will not influence the first shell, and once λ_1 is known we can evaluate $G_{(2)}$. This $G_{(2)}$ is then used to determine λ_2 — the only available parameter in the electron density of the second shell — from the variational principle. Continuing we can determine all λ_m and finally from all $n_{(m)}(r)$ the total electron density $n(r)$. Although this method involves a large amount of computational work, it is straightforward and certainly much simpler than the self-consistent field method. Gombás and Ladányi have used this method for Ne, A, Kr, X, and Rb$^+$ and find results in excellent agreement with results obtained by Hartree and co-workers using the more cumbersome self-consistent field method.

In conclusion we wish to mention briefly to what physical problems the statistical method has been applied. For detailed discussions of applications we must refer to the review articles of Gombás (1956) and March (1957). In the case of atoms, apart from providing a rough idea of the electron distribution which can be used as a starting point for the Hartree-Fock method, the statistical method can be used to obtain such quantities as the average orbital angular momentum of the electrons, the atomic binding energies, atomic and ionic radii, diamagnetic susceptibilities,

polarizabilities, and scattering cross sections for X-rays.
In the case of molecules, the Hartree-Fock method is very
difficult, although recent work by Roothaan and Löwdin
has made its application much easier and the statistical
method has, therefore, been used to obtain electronic
densities and such properties as force constants. Interesting
results are also obtained in the case of solids, especially
ionic crystals and metals. The statistical theory has been
used to calculate cohesive energies, momentum distributions
of electrons in metals, and it has also been used for the
discussion of impurities (see Friedel 1954, Dingle 1955,
Mansfield 1956, March 1957) and such related topics as
resistivity of dilute alloys, diffusion, and the structure of
dislocations. The main application of the statistical theory,
and the one where its use is most fully justified, has been
in the field of matter under high pressure. In the cases of
practical interest it is often no longer justified to assume
that the temperature is essentially zero, and one of the
problems to be solved is to find the equation of state of the
material, both in the case of complete and of incomplete
degeneracy. The main field of application has up to now
been that of geophysics, although shock-wave techniques
seem now slowly to become extended to produce pressures
which are sufficiently high for the statistical method to be
applicable.

CHAPTER 4

The Nuclear Many-Body Problem

In Chapter 2 we discussed the Hartree-Fock method. In general this method is mainly applicable to the case where the interaction between the particles is weak. Recently, however, it has been found that an extension and improvement of the Hartree method can be used to deal with the nucleus, even though nuclear forces are strong and short range. In the present chapter we shall discuss this theory, due to Brueckner, in the second section using a derivation of the Brueckner equations based on perturbation theory. In the first section we give a brief introduction to the nuclear many-body problem.

4.1 Introduction

In considering the properties of nuclei we come across two kinds of behaviour which at first sight seem to be in direct contradiction to one another. On the one hand we have evidence that the nucleus can be treated as a liquid drop. This idea was first suggested by Bohr (1936a, b, Bohr and Kalckar 1937) and on this basis Bohr and Wheeler (1939) explained the fission process (see also Hill and Wheeler 1953). This model also seems to give the correct energy level density at about 10 MeV (see Bethe 1937, Wergeland 1945, ter Haar 1949) and leads to the surface energy term in the Weizsäcker (1935) formula for the nuclear binding energy. On the other hand there is the vast amount of evidence in favour of the nuclear shell model (Mayer 1948) which seems to suggest that for some properties of the nucleus (nuclear spin, nuclear magnetic moments, magic

number nuclei) the nucleons can be considered to behave
as independent particles. In the same category also falls
the success of the cloudy crystal ball model of the nucleus
(Feshbach, Porter, and Weisskopf 1955).

The success of the nuclear shell model is really most
amazing, as nuclear forces seem to be strong and with a
range comparable to the mean distance apart of the nucleons in the nucleus. The first clue to a solution of this
difficulty was given by Weisskopf (1951) who drew attention
to the analogous problem in the case of the conduction
electrons in a metal. In both cases the Pauli principle
restricts the possible results of collisions to such an extent
that we are left with a system showing nearly independent
particle behaviour.

In the nuclear case Brueckner and collaborators
(Brueckner 1954, 1955a, b, Brueckner, Levinson, and
Mahmoud 1954, Brueckner and Levinson 1955, Brueckner,
Eden, and Francis 1955, Eden and Francis 1955, see also
Eden 1956, 1958, Bethe 1956, Tobocman 1957, Kromhout
1957, Goldstone 1957, Kümmel 1957a, b, Brenig 1957),
have developed a modified Hartree-Fock theory for the
nucleus which will be discussed in the next section and which
gives a basis for the shell model. On the other hand, in
Chapter 9 we shall discuss theories which pay due attention
to the collective behaviour of nuclei and also briefly discuss
the possible interaction between collective and particle
modes — which is important for a discussion of nuclear
quadrupole moments.

4.2   Brueckner's Theory

In the space at our disposal we clearly cannot discuss
all aspects of the Brueckner theory, or even begin such a discussion. We shall, however, briefly sketch how the Brueckner
theory can be derived from ordinary perturbation theory,
following a recent paper by Kümmel (1957b). For a discussion of the equations and of the many difficulties involved

we refer to the rapidly expanding literature (see especially Bethe 1956, Eden 1958).

We start once again from the many-body Schrödinger equation,

$$HΨ = EΨ, \ H = \sum_j T_j + \tfrac{1}{2} \sum_{j \neq n} U_{jn}, \quad (4.201)$$

where T_j is the kinetic energy of the jth particle and U_{jn} the potential energy of the interaction between the jth and the nth particle. In the nuclear case U_{jn} may be velocity dependent, which means that it must always be considered to be an operator, even if we use ordinary position coordinates as the variables on which the wave function depends. In writing down equation 4.201 we have assumed that we may neglect three- and more-body forces.

Let us assume that we know how to solve a similarly constructed Schrödinger equation

$$H_M Φ = EΦ, \ H_{M!} = \sum_j T_j + \tfrac{1}{2} \sum_{j \neq n} V_{jn}, \quad (4.202)$$

where for the moment V_{jn} is not yet defined. We shall later require that equation 4.202 can be solved by the Hartree-Fock method so that we can find solutions $Φ$ in the form of determinants built up out of single particle wave functions. Equation 4.202 will be called the *model equation*. We shall now assume that we may write

$$H = H_M + H', \ H' = \tfrac{1}{2} \sum_{j \neq n} [U_{jn} - V_{jn}], \quad (4.203)$$

where H' may be treated as a perturbing energy. This means that we assume that the model, which leads to a shell-model wave function, is a fair approximation to the nuclear system under consideration.

Let $Φ_\rho$ be an eigenfunction of H_M corresponding to the eigenvalue E_ρ and let $Ψ_\rho$ be the corresponding eigenfunction of H with an eigenvalue $E_\rho + Δ$, that is, corresponding to an energy shift $Δ$. We are interested both in this energy shift, and in $Ψ_\rho$. Let F be the operator producing $Ψ_\rho$ from $Φ_\rho$,

$$Ψ_\rho = FΦ_\rho. \quad (4.204)$$

Using a slight modification of the Chew-Goldberger, (1952) form of the Brillouin-Wigner perturbation theory, one finds for F the equation

$$F = 1 + \tfrac{1}{2}Q \sum_{j \neq n}(V'_{jn} - V_{jn}) F_{jn}, \qquad (4.205)$$

$$F_{jn} = 1 + \tfrac{1}{2}Q \sum_{p \neq q\,(pq \neq jn)}(V'_{pq} - V_{pq}) F_{pq}, \qquad (4.206)$$

$$V'_{jn} = U'_{jn} + (U'_{jn} - V_{jn})\, Q(V'_n - V_{jn}), \qquad (4.207)$$

$$U'_{jn} = U_{jn} - \Delta_{jn}, \;\; \Delta_{jn} = \left(\begin{matrix} A \\ 2 \end{matrix}\right)^{-1} \Delta, \qquad (4.208)$$

where A is the number of nucleons present and the operator, Q, is defined by the equation

$$Q\Phi_\sigma = (1 - \delta_{\rho\sigma})(E_\rho - H_{\mathrm{M}})^{-1}\, \Phi_\sigma. \qquad (4.209)$$

The energy shift Δ is given by the equation

$$\Delta = [\tfrac{1}{2}\sum_{j \neq n}(V'_{jn} + \Delta_{jn} - V_{jn})F_{jn}]_{\rho\rho}, \qquad (4.210)$$

where $\Omega_{\rho\sigma}$ indicates the matrix elements of the operator Ω.

Equations 4.201 to 4.210 are still exact. The choice of V_{jn} is usually made in such a way that (i) Δ is as small as possible, (ii) as many matrix elements $(F - 1)_{\rho\sigma}$ as possible are zero, and (iii) equation 4.202 can be solved using the Hartree-Fock method. The first two conditions imply that we want the model to be close replica of the nuclear system, and the last condition is one of expediency. Conditions (i) and (ii) could be satisfied by choosing $V_{jn} = U_{jn}$, but then condition (iii) would not be satisfied. One is thus led to look for a compromise. We refer to Bethe's article for a discussion of this difficulty.

The V'_{jn} satisfying equation 4.207 is the so-called *reaction matrix* which describes the interaction between two particles. Equation 4.207 can unfortunately not be solved, and in looking for simplifications one is led to the Brueckner equations. These equations are obtained by dropping V_{jn} out of this equation, that is, by using instead of equation 4.207 the equation

$$V'_{jn} = U'_{jn} + U'_{jn} Q V'_{jn} . \qquad (4.211)$$

One can show (Bethe 1956, Kümmel 1957b) that in doing this one neglects terms of the order A^{-1}.

One might ask in how far the Brueckner theory is useful. One can point to its success in calculating to a fair approximation nuclear binding energies. It has also been used to discuss the nuclear surface energy (Skyrme 1956) the spin-orbit potential (Kisslinger 1956; see, however, Jancovici 1957), and high-energy nuclear reactions (Eden 1958). However, one really would like to know in how far it provides us with a justification of the shell model. The model wave function Φ is a shell-model wave function, but the real nuclear wave function Ψ has only a very small admixture of Φ (see Bethe 1956). However, if the energy shifts Δ are small the Brueckner theory does provide a justification for the formation of stable closed-shell configurations in as far as both the model and the nuclear system will show similar discontinuities in binding energy near closed-shell configurations. Also the Brueckner model justifies to some extent the use of smoothed-out nucleon-nucleon potentials in shell-model calculations instead of hard-core potentials which fit free nucleon scattering data.

Finally we must draw attention to the fact that the Brueckner theory presents us with a considerable improvement of the ordinary Hartree-Fock method. In the latter, one considers single particles in the field of all the other particles, but in the Brueckner theory one evaluates the interaction between pairs of particles exactly and only the influence of the $A - 2$ other particles is smoothed out. This extension of the self-consistent field method might well become of importance in other fields of many-body physics. It is of interest to note that Brenig (1957), has discussed the Brueckner theory starting from the more conventional many-body theory.

CHAPTER 5

Quasi-particles in Solids

In this chapter we discuss holes, excitons, polarons, and excitarons in solids. As the effective mass concept is essential for the discussion of quasi-particles, it is treated at some length in the first section. This approximation is then used, first in Section 2 to discuss excitons, which are correlated electron-hole pairs in insulators, and second in Section 3 to discuss polarons, which are electrons in polar substances surrounded by a phonon cloud which is responsible for a polarization field producing a sort of self-dug hole for the electron. We also mention briefly the excitaron (Meyer 1956a, b) which is an exciton in a polar medium accompanied by a phonon cloud.

5.1   The Effective Mass Approximation

We mentioned in Chapter I that in many respects the system of conduction electrons in metals or semiconductors can be treated as a system of free Fermi-Dirac particles, but with a mass which is not equal to the free electron mass. In the present section we wish to discuss the concept of an *effective mass* in somewhat more detail. Basically the situation is very simple. If there is some physical quantity Q which for a free particle system depends on the mass m of the particles in a certain way,

$$Q = f(m), \qquad (5.101)$$

and if in the case of a metal or semiconductor this quantity is found to have the value Q_0, say, corresponding to a value of m equal to m_0, m_0 is said to be the effective mass of the particles corresponding to this particular quantity for the particular substance considered. We notice first of all that in order that the idea of an effective mass can be successfully applied, it is clearly necessary that m_0 is practically the same for as many different quantities Q as possible. Among the Q used to determine m_0 we may mention specific heat coefficients, cyclotron resonance frequencies, thermoelectric power, mobilities, magnetic susceptibilities, and dielectric constants (for a survey of the determination of m_0 in the case of semiconductors see, for instance, Seraphin 1955).

We shall begin our discussion with the conventional method of introducing the effective mass by considering the relations between electron velocity and energy on the one hand, and acceleration and external field on the other hand, using wave-packet methods and considering the case of a periodic lattice, which for the sake of simplicity we shall assume to be of cubic symmetry (see, for instance, Seitz 1940, § 68). The Hamiltonian of our system is of the form

$$H = -\frac{\hbar^2}{2m} \sum_j \mathbf{\nabla}_j{}^2 - \sum_{j,\,l} \frac{Z_l e^2}{|\mathbf{x}_j - \mathbf{X}_l|} + \tfrac{1}{2}\sum_{j\neq n} \frac{e^2}{r_{jn}}, \quad (5.102)$$

where Z_l and $\mathbf{X}_l$ are respectively the charge and position coordinate of the lth nucleus, and where $\mathbf{x}_j$ is the position coordinate of the jth electron. To simplify our considerations we assume the nuclei to be at rest at their lattice positions. We discuss the complete many-body Hamiltonian in Appendix C, but for the moment we want to simplify our considerations even more by assuming that it will be a fair approximation to treat the electrons as being free particles moving in a periodic potential, U_{per}, that is, satisfying the Schrödinger equation

$$H\psi = E\psi, \quad H = -(\hbar^2/2m)\mathbf{\nabla}^2 + U_{\text{per}}(\mathbf{x}). \quad (5.103)$$

It is well known (for instance, Kramers 1935, Seitz 1940 Ch. VIII, Dekker 1957 Ch. 10) that equation 5.103 possesses solutions, so-called Bloch functions (Bloch 1928), which are plane waves modulated by a function which has the same periodicity as the lattice,

$$\psi = \exp\left[\pm i(\mathbf{k} \cdot \mathbf{x})\right]u_{\mathbf{k}}(\mathbf{x}). \qquad (5.104)$$

Moreover, the energy $E(\mathbf{k})$ as a function of $\mathbf{k}$ shows band structure, that is, there are energy regions corresponding to normalizable wave functions — which are of the form of equation 5.104 — separated by energy regions corresponding to solutions which behave exponentially. These energy regions are referred to as "allowed" and "forbidden" bands respectively.

Let us now consider the one-dimensional case of an electron characterized by a wave-packet centred around a wave number k'. This wave-packet will be described by a wave function $\chi(x, t)$ of the form (compare Kramers 1957, equation 1.42)

$$\chi(x,\ t) = \int A(k)u_k(x) \exp\left[ikx - iE(k)t/\hbar\right]dk, \qquad (5.105)$$

where we have included the time dependence of the Bloch functions and where the amplitude function $A(k)$ is a peak function with a maximum for $k = k'$. We put

$$k = k' + \Delta k, \qquad (5.106)$$

and assume that the maximum of $A(k)$ is so sharp that we may write

$$E(k) \doteqdot E(k') + \Delta k(dE/dk). \qquad (5.107)$$

Substituting expression 5.107 into equation 5.105 and using the fact that u_k varies only slowly with k we have

$$\chi(x,\ t) \doteqdot u_{k'} \exp\left[ik'x - iE(k')t/\hbar\right] \cdot$$

$$\int A(\Delta k) \exp\left[i\Delta kx - t(dE/dk)/\hbar\right]d\Delta k. \qquad (5.108)$$

We see that $\chi(x, t)$ is the Bloch function for $k = k'$ multiplied by a factor which has constant amplitude at those points for which $x - t(dE/dk)/\hbar$ is constant. This means that the wave-packet — or the electron characterized by the wave-packet — moves with a velocity v given by the equation

$$v = (dE/dk)/\hbar. \tag{5.109}$$

The acceleration a of the electron is now given by the equation

$$a = \frac{dv}{dt} = \frac{1}{\hbar}\frac{d}{dk}\left(\frac{dE}{dt}\right). \tag{5.110}$$

We can use the theorem of Ehrenfest (1927) to prove in the case of an electron characterized by a wave-packet the validity of the classical relation

$$dE/dt = Fv, \tag{5.111}$$

where F is the applied force. Using equations 5.109 to 5.111 we end up with the relation

$$a = \frac{d^2 E}{dk^2}\frac{F}{\hbar^2}, \tag{5.112}$$

and, as one example of equation 5.101 is Newton's relation between mass, acceleration, and applied force, we find

$$m_0 = \hbar^2(d^2E/dk^2)^{-1}. \tag{5.113}$$

We see that in general m_0 will depend on k. If we consider energies near the lower edge of a band and if we consider a solid of cubic symmetry (we do not wish to discuss the complication of anisotropic effective masses), the energy can be written in the form

$$E = E_e + \tfrac{1}{2}Ak^2, \tag{5.114}$$

where E_e is the energy at the edge of the band. Combining equations 5.113 and 5.114 we find

$$m_0 = \hbar^2/A. \tag{5.115}$$

Equation 5.114 is another instance of a relation like equation 5.101, as we can use equations 5.109 and 5.115 to write it in the form

$$E - E_e = \tfrac{1}{2}m_0 v^2. \tag{5.116}$$

We saw that an electron moving in a periodic potential behaves under the influence of an external force as if it were a particle of inertial mass m_0, where m_0 is given by equation 5.113. This expression will in general be different from m, and may even under certain circumstances (near the top of a band) become negative. In the last case an external force in a certain direction will lead to an acceleration in the opposite direction, and one talks of "holes." That this nomenclature is more than a mere taking into account of a change in sign of m_0 follows from Heisenberg's considerations (1931) which showed that one can replace the wave equation for electrons near the top of a filled band by a wave equation for positively charged particles in an empty band.

We want to consider the difference between m and m_0 in slightly more detail, using once again the Ehrenfest theorem (see Pfirsch and Spenke 1954, Seraphin 1955). We get in that way for the quantum mechanical average of the electron acceleration the equation (see, for instance, Kramers 1957, p. 112)

$$ma = -\,\partial U/\partial x. \qquad (5.117)$$

In the case of an electron in a lattice, the right-hand side consists of two contributions, first of all the external force F and secondly $\partial U_{per}/\partial x$, so that we get

$$ma = F - \partial U_{per}/\partial x\,, \qquad (5.118)$$

or, using the relation $m_0 a = F$

$$\frac{m}{m_0} = 1 - \frac{1}{F}\,\frac{\partial U_{per}}{\partial x}. \qquad (5.119)$$

We see here at once the relation between the difference between m and m_0, and the influence of the lattice (see also Kittel 1954). It is possible to evaluate the quantum mechanical average of the right-hand side of equation 5.119, and the result is expression 5.113 for m_0.

One of the most successful applications of the effective

mass concept has been in the discussion of the influence
of donors and acceptors in semiconductors. Let us for the
sake of simplicity assume that we are dealing with an insulator with N electrons, and let us add to this system one
electron — which will thus in the ground state occupy the
lowest state of the conduction band — and replace one of
the nuclei in the lattice by one with a charge larger than that
of the original nucleus (donor). This replacement will have
as a consequence the introduction of an extra (nonperiodic)
term in the potential energy. It can be shown that to a
first approximation the behaviour of the last electron can
be described by a Schrödinger equation with a Hamiltonian
H given by the equation

$$H = - \frac{\hbar^2}{2m_0} \nabla^2 - \frac{e^2}{\varepsilon r}, \qquad (5.120)$$

where ε is the dielectric constant of the material, and where
we have assumed the donor atom to be situated at the
origin. The point of interest at this moment is that the
effective mass m_0 enters into this equation and not the
free mass m. One can even go one step further and show
that if the potential energy in the crystal can be written
in the form

$$U = U_{\text{per}} + U_1, \qquad (5.121)$$

where U_1 is a slowly varying function, that is, $|\nabla U_1|$ is small
compared to $|U_1|/d$ (d: lattice parameter), the wave func-
tion of an electron with an energy near a band edge can be
written in the form

$$\phi = \psi\chi, \qquad (5.122)$$

where ψ is a solution of equation 5.103 given by expression
5.104 with $\mathbf{k} = \mathbf{k}_e$, and where χ satisfies the equation

$$- (\hbar^2/2m_0)\nabla^2\chi + U_1\chi = (E - E_e)\chi. \qquad (5.123)$$

Equation 5.120 is a special case of this more general one,
as is shown in Appendix C. In that appendix we also derive

the Hamiltonian of equation 5.120 by a method due to Kohn (1957) based on the many-body Hamiltonian of equation 5.102. The proof of equation 5.123 is based on a one-electron picture, and we refer to a discussion by James (1949a, b; see also Slater 1949) for this proof and for a discussion of the applications of this equation to donor, acceptor, and surface states.

5.2   Excitons

In the last two sections of this chapter we shall consider some of the quasi-particles of modern solid-state physics. In the preceding section we saw how interactions — in that case the interactions of an electron with a periodic potential — can to a certain extent be taken into account by replacing the interacting particle by a free (quasi-) particle with an effective mass different from the free mass of the original particle. The introduction of an effective mass to take care of interactions was also discussed in Chapter 1. In that chapter we also noted that the importance of introducing quasi-particles lies mainly in the fact that we can, to a fair approximation, describe the behaviour of a system of interacting particles by that of a system of free quasi-particles. In the present section we discuss excitons and in the next section polarons.

In insulators it is found that light may be absorbed without producing photoconductivity. At first sight this may be surprising. As we are dealing with an insulator we would expect that the valence band is completely filled and that the conduction band, separated from the valence band by a finite energy gap ΔE, is completely empty. Absorption of light would mean the ejection of an electron from the valence band into the conduction band, and we would expect that this would lead to photoconductivity, as the ejected electron is free to move through the lattice. We now, first of all, note that the ejection of the electron will leave a hole in the valence band. If we used a very simple one-electron picture we would expect absorption to start at an energy

ΔE corresponding to the creation of a hole at the top of the valence band and leaving the electron at the bottom of the conduction band. It is found, however, that there exist in many cases discrete energies of absorption less than ΔE. These derive from the interaction between the hole and the electron which can form a pair. This pair, which can move freely through the lattice, is called an *exciton*, and it possesses discrete, bound energy states. Frenkel (1931a, b; see also Peierls 1932) first suggested the existence of excitons and Wannier (1937) introduced the so-called Wannier-functions to describe their occurrence in ionic crystals. In that case, and especially in the case of molecular crystals, one may assume that to a first approximation the wave function of the system can be written as a product (or linear combination of products) of wave functions centred on the nuclei in the crystal. The exciton states are then closely connected to the energy levels of the atoms constituting the crystal. On the other hand, in the case of semiconductors one must start rather from the band structure picture, as we shall do presently. Before doing this we wish to refer the reader to survey articles by Slater (1954), Pekar (1956), Meyer (1956a, b), and Haken (1958) for a more detailed discussion of various aspects of exciton theory.

From the foregoing discussion it is clear that instead of dealing with a one-particle problem, we are dealing with a two-particle one. It is assumed that both the electron and the hole may be described by the effective mass approximation, and in the case of cubical symmetry we can ascribe to each of them one effective mass, m_{el} and m_h. The Hamiltonian H determining their behaviour will be

$$H = -\frac{\hbar^2}{2\,m_{el}}\,\nabla_{el}{}^2 - \frac{\hbar^2}{2m_h}\nabla^2{}_h - \frac{e^2}{\varepsilon\,|x_{el} - x_h|}, \quad (5.201)$$

where ε is the static dielectric constant of the material.

We shall now assume that the valence and conduction bands are nondegenerate, and introduce the transformation to centre-of-mass and relative coordinates,

$$\mathbf{X} = (m_{\mathrm{el}}\,\mathbf{x}_{\mathrm{el}} + m_{\mathrm{h}}\,\mathbf{x}_{\mathrm{h}})/(m_{\mathrm{el}} + m_{\mathrm{h}}), \quad \mathbf{x} = \mathbf{x}_{\mathrm{el}} - \mathbf{x}_{\mathrm{h}}, \quad (5.202)$$

which leads to the Schrödinger equation

$$\left[-\frac{\hbar^2}{2M}\,\boldsymbol{\nabla}_x^{\,2} - \frac{\hbar^2}{2\mu}\,\boldsymbol{\nabla}_x^{\,2} - \frac{e^2}{\varepsilon|\mathbf{x}|}\right]\Psi = E\Psi, \quad \mu = \frac{m_{\mathrm{el}}\,m_{\mathrm{h}}}{M},$$
$$M = m_{\mathrm{el}} + m_{\mathrm{h}}, \quad (5.203)$$

with the solutions

$$\Psi = e^{i(\mathbf{K}\cdot\mathbf{X})}\,\varphi_n(\mathbf{x}), \quad E = \frac{\hbar^2 K^2}{2M} - \frac{\mu e^4}{2\hbar^2\,\varepsilon^2\,n^2}. \quad (5.204)$$

The solutions in equation 5.204 correspond to an exciton moving with a velocity $\hbar\mathbf{K}/M$ through the lattice, its internal structure given by the hydrogen wave function φ_n. In the ground state φ_n is given by the equation

$$\varphi_1(\mathbf{x}) = C\exp\left(-r/a_0\right), \quad a_0 = \varepsilon\hbar^2/\mu e^2, \quad (5.205)$$

where C is a normalizing constant. The quantity a_0 may be called the radius of the exciton and is about $\tfrac{1}{2}\varepsilon$ angstoms.

Let us briefly discuss our results. As the hole and the electron are bound together, the creation of an exciton cannot lead to conductivity, as the exciton is a neutral entity. We might ask whether the use of the effective mass approximation is justified. We have in our discussion made the assumption of cubical symmetry and nondegenerate bands. These restrictions are, however, not essential, and Dresselhaus (1956) has used the effective mass approximation to discuss the case of degenerate, nonspherical energy bands. However, there is another restriction to the use of the effective mass approach, namely, the requirement that the perturbing potential must be sufficiently smooth. This means in the present case, that the dielectric constant must be sufficiently large. In that case the exciton radius will be large compared to the lattice parameters. Dresselhaus found that, indeed, ε must be at least eight in order that his calculations would be valid.

In our discussions we have assumed that the lattice

is pure periodic. In such a case there will be no localized excitons. Indeed, one can show (for instance Haken 1955b) that the periodicity of the lattice excludes the possibility of a localized state. However, if there are imperfections present this is no longer true, and in many crystals, especially the alkali halides, excitons occur which show a large degree of localization. There is a large literature on the subject of these localized excitons, (see for instance, Seitz 1954 for references; see also Muto and Okuno 1956, 1957, Bassani and Inchauspé 1957, Martienssen 1957) and their diffusion (Trlifaj 1956, Hrivnák 1957, Diemer and Hoogenstraten 1957). There is also a large literature on excitons in Cu_2O (Gross, Zaharchenia, and Reinov 1954, Nikitine, Perny, and Sieskind 1954), where a hydrogen-like spectrum has, indeed, been observed; in HgI_2 (Nikitine 1955, Gross and Kaplianskii 1955, Gross, Kaplianskii, and Novikov 1956); in CdS (Gross and Jacobson 1955, Gross, Kaplianskii, and Novikov 1956); in PbI_2 and CdI_2 (Nikitine 1956); and in CuI (Nikitine, Reiss, and Perny 1956). Gross and collaborators (Gross, Zaharchenia, and Reinov 1954, 1956) have also studied the fine structure and Zeeman effect of the exciton lines. Most of the papers mentioned here contain further references.

Although the formation of an exciton does not lead directly to photoconductivity, it can do so indirectly. It is possible that there are in the crystal impurity centres which are keeping electrons trapped. If the energy needed to release such a trapped electron is less than the binding energy of the exciton, the electron-hole pair may, after migrating to such an impurity centre, recombine, releasing in the process sufficient energy to set the trapped electron free and thus produce photoconductivity. Such processes have been observed experimentally.

In order to understand these processes theoretically it is necessary to possess a theory of the mobility of the exciton. This mobility is determined by the mean free path of the exciton, which in turn is determined by the inter-

action of the exciton with the lattice vibrations — in the
case of a polar crystal with the optical branch (Haken
1956c) and in the case of a nonpolar crystal with the
acoustical branch of the vibrational spectrum (Anselm and
Firsov 1955).   The interaction of an exciton with the
lattice vibrations may under certain circumstances be so
strong as to lead to a new quasi-particle, the so-called
excitaron (Meyer 1956a, b).   We refer to a series of papers
by Haken (1953, 1954a, b, 1955a, b, 1956a–e, 1957, 1958,
Trlifaj 1957) for a discussion of excitons in polar crystals
and further references.

5.3   Polarons

In this section we shall be concerned with polar crystals.
One way of describing a dielectric is in terms of a polarization
field.   An electron moving in such a medium will on the one
hand be under the influence of this field, while on the
other hand its electric field will influence the polarization
field.   The final result will be an electron surrounded by a
self-induced polarization field.   This quasi-particle is called
a polaron (Pekar 1946).   The theory of polarons is of
interest not only because of its application to solid-state
problems, but also because it is a simple example of the
treatment of the interaction between a particle and a
quantized field.   There are at present available a number
of excellent reviews to which we refer for a detailed discussion (Pekar 1953, 1954, Fröhlich 1954, Haken 1955a,
Allcock 1956).   Our discussion will be largely based on
Schultz's MIT thesis (1956), where one can also find a
comprehensive bibliography.

The retinue of phonons which change an electron into
a polaron has many consequences.   First of all the elec-
trostatic energy of the electron in the deformed polarized
lattice will be larger than the energy necessary to produce
the deformation, and the polaron state will thus correspond
to a lower energy than the state of the bare electron in the
undeformed lattice.   The net gain in energy is called the

polaron self-energy. This energy will depend on the velocity of the polaron. For very small velocities, the energy will to a first approximation be given by the equation

$$E_{pol} = E_0 + p^2/2m_{pol}, \qquad (5.301)$$

where p is the polaron momentum, m_{pol} the polaron effective mass, defined by equation 5.301 and where we have assumed cubical symmetry. The polaron effective mass will in general be different from the effective mass of an electron without its retinue of phonons. Two more properties which will depend on the deformed polarization environment are the mobility and the absorption spectrum of a polaron. In the present section, however, we do not have the space to discuss all aspects and we shall concentrate on the self-energy and effective mass. As far as the latter is concerned, it is of interest to note that the effective mass defined by equation 5.301 will also be the mass entering into Newton's third law (compare the discussion in Section 5.1; see also Haken 1953).

The first thing we must do is to find the Hamiltonian of the system, electron + polarizable medium. In doing this we shall introduce a number of simplifications and at the same time find the parameters which determine the strength of the interaction between the electron and the polarization. We shall use a classical approach, as all features which we wish to discuss will be present in that case and the formalism will be simpler than the quantum mechanical one. We first of all take the periodic potential into account by ascribing to the electron an effective mass m_0. The use of the effective mass approximation immediately restricts our discussion to slow electrons. Secondly, we shall assume that the intrinsic or core electrons will follow perfectly both the ionic displacements involved in the lattice vibrations and the electric field produced by the motion of the slow electron. The polarization field $P(x)$ will correspond to an ionic displacement with the core electrons adjusted to this displacement. In evaluating the potential energy corresponding to the field $P(x)$ we may assume that the displacement field $\mathbf{D}(\mathbf{x})$, related to $\mathbf{P}$ by the equation

$$\mathbf{D} = \varepsilon\mathbf{E} = \mathbf{E} + 4\pi\mathbf{P}, \tag{5.302}$$

where ε is the static dielectric constant and $\mathbf{E}$ the electric field, is equal to zero, corresponding to the absence of free charges in the crystal. The polarization due to the extra electron is now assumed to be produced in two steps. First of all we put on an external field $\mathbf{E}_1$ corresponding to $\mathbf{D}_1$ and $\mathbf{P}_1$. This field is switched on so slowly that equations 5.302 hold. Then $\mathbf{E}_1$ is switched off so quickly that the ionic cores stay put, but the electrons adjust themselves to the new field, where now $\mathbf{D} = 0$ and $\mathbf{P}$ is equal to the polarization field produced by the extra electron. In the first stage equations 5.302 hold, and we have during the switching on of the field

$$\mathbf{P} = \frac{\varepsilon - 1}{4\pi\varepsilon}\,\mathbf{D}, \tag{5.303}$$

and the total energy per unit volume needed to produce the field $\mathbf{E}_1$ is given by the equation

$$\int_0^{\mathbf{P}_1}(\mathbf{D}\cdot d\mathbf{P}) = \frac{\varepsilon - 1}{8\pi\varepsilon}\,\mathbf{D}_1{}^2. \tag{5.304}$$

In the second stage we have instead of equation 5.303 the relation

$$d\mathbf{P} = \frac{n^2 - 1}{4\pi n^2}\,d\mathbf{D}, \tag{5.305}$$

where n is the refractive index of the material (strictly speaking for light of a wave length just above the maximum wave length of the absorption due to the core electrons; n^2 is equal to the high-frequency dielectric constant ε_∞). The energy gained per unit volume during the switching off is given by the equation

$$\int_{\mathbf{D}_1}^0(\mathbf{D}\cdot d\mathbf{P}) = -\frac{n^2 - 1}{8\pi n^2}\,\mathbf{D}_1{}^2, \tag{5.306}$$

and the final value of $\mathbf{P}$ is given by the equation

$$\mathbf{P} = \mathbf{P}_1 + \int_{\mathbf{D}_1}^{0} d\mathbf{P} = \mathbf{D}_1/4\pi c, \qquad (5.307)$$

where c is an "effective" dielectric constant given by the equation

$$\frac{1}{c} = \frac{1}{n^2} - \frac{1}{\varepsilon}. \qquad (5.308)$$

Combining equations 5.304, 5.306, and 5.307 we find for the total potential energy of the polarization field $U_{\mathbf{P}}$ the expression

$$U_{\mathbf{P}} = 2\pi c \int \mathbf{P}^2 \, d^3 \mathbf{x}. \qquad (5.309)$$

We shall now make an additional assumption, namely that we can neglect all acoustic and all transverse optical lattice modes, and that the longitudinal optical modes show no dispersion, that is, all possess the same frequency ω. In that case, the kinetic energy of the polarization field $T_{\mathbf{P}}$ is simply given by the expression

$$T_{\mathbf{P}} = (2\pi c/\omega^2) \int \dot{\mathbf{P}}^2 \, d^3 \mathbf{x}. \qquad (5.310)$$

(The relationship between equations 5.309 and 5.310 is that between the potential and kinetic energy of a simple harmonic oscillator of frequency ω.)

We finally have to find the interaction energy of the electron of charge $-e$ at $\mathbf{x}'$ and the field $\mathbf{P}(\mathbf{x})$. If $\mathbf{D}'$ is the displacement due to the electron we have

$$\mathbf{D}'(\mathbf{x}) = -\nabla \frac{e}{|\mathbf{x}' - \mathbf{x}|}, \qquad (5.311)$$

and the interaction energy H_{int} is given by the equation

$$H_{\text{int}} = -\int (\mathbf{D}' \cdot \mathbf{P}) \, d^3 \mathbf{x} = e \int \left(\mathbf{P}(\mathbf{x}) \cdot \nabla \frac{1}{|\mathbf{x} - \mathbf{x}'|} \right) d^3 \mathbf{x}. \qquad (5.312)$$

Let $\mathbf{Q}(\mathbf{x})$ be canonically conjugate to $\mathbf{P}(\mathbf{x})$,

$$\mathbf{Q} = (4\pi c/\omega^2)\dot{\mathbf{P}}, \qquad (5.313)$$

and let **p** be the electron momentum. Combining equations
5.309, 5.310, 5.312, and 5.313 we get for the total Hamiltonian H of our system the equation

$$H = \frac{\mathbf{p}^2}{2m_0} + e\int\left(\mathbf{P}(\mathbf{x}) \cdot \nabla \frac{1}{|\mathbf{x} - \mathbf{x}'|}\right) d^3\mathbf{x}$$
$$+ \int\left(\frac{\mathbf{Q}^2}{2M_{\mathrm{P}}} + \tfrac{1}{2}M_{\mathrm{P}}\,\omega^2\,\mathbf{P}^2\right) d^3\mathbf{x}, \tag{5.314}$$

where

$$M_{\mathrm{P}} = 4\pi c/\omega^2. \tag{5.315}$$

Before discussing the Hamiltonian of equation 5.314
we wish to write it in a different form. We first of all
decompose **P** in plane waves, and assuming once again
that our system is within a unit volume we write

$$\mathbf{P}(\mathbf{x}) = (2M_{\mathrm{P}}\,\omega)^{-\frac{1}{2}} \sum_{\mathbf{k}}(\mathbf{k}/k)(a_{\mathbf{k}} + b_{-\mathbf{k}}) \exp i(\mathbf{k}\cdot\mathbf{x}), \tag{5.316}$$

where $a_{\mathbf{k}}$ is canonically conjugate to $ib_{\mathbf{k}}$. Expressed in the
$a_{\mathbf{k}}$ and $b_{\mathbf{k}}$ the Hamiltonian of equation 5.314 is given by
the equation

$$H = \frac{\mathbf{p}^2}{2m_0} + \sum_{\mathbf{k}} \frac{C}{k}[a_{\mathbf{k}}e^{i(\mathbf{k}\cdot\mathbf{x})} + b_{\mathbf{k}}e^{-i(\mathbf{k}\cdot\mathbf{x})}] + \sum_{\mathbf{k}} \omega\, a_{\mathbf{k}} b_{\mathbf{k}}, \tag{5.317}$$

which can be derived by the usual methods of classical
mechanics. In equation 5.317, C is given by the equation

$$C = 4\pi e(2M_{\mathrm{P}}\,\omega)^{-\frac{1}{2}} = e(2\pi\omega/c)^{\frac{1}{2}}. \tag{5.318}$$

We now perform a canonical transformation from **x**,
p, $a_{\mathbf{k}}$, $b_{\mathbf{k}}$ to **x**′, **p**′, $\alpha_{\mathbf{k}}$, $\beta_{\mathbf{k}}$ using the generating function Ω,
given by the equation

$$\Omega = (\mathbf{x} \cdot \mathbf{p}') + \sum_{\mathbf{k}} \alpha_{\mathbf{k}}\,\beta_{-\mathbf{k}} \exp i(\mathbf{k}\cdot\mathbf{x}), \tag{5.319}$$

and the transformation equations

$$\mathbf{p} = \frac{\partial\Omega}{\partial\mathbf{x}}, \quad b_{\mathbf{k}} = \frac{\partial\Omega}{\partial a_{\mathbf{k}}}, \quad \mathbf{x}' = \frac{\partial\Omega}{\partial\mathbf{p}'}, \quad \alpha_{\mathbf{k}} = \frac{\partial\Omega}{\partial\beta_{\mathbf{k}}}. \tag{5.320}$$

The result of this transformation is

$$H = \frac{(\mathbf{p}' - \sum \mathbf{k}\,\alpha_{\mathbf{k}}\beta_{\mathbf{k}})^2}{2m_0} + \sum \frac{C}{k}\,(\alpha_{\mathbf{k}} + \beta_{\mathbf{k}}) + \sum \omega\alpha_{\mathbf{k}}\beta_{\mathbf{k}}. \quad (5.321)$$

Let us now consider for a moment the interaction term. Whether or not the coupling between the electron and the lattice vibrations will be strong will depend on the magnitude of the constant C. From C and the quantities $\hbar\omega$, ω^{-1}, and m_0, which are the natural units of energy, time, and mass for our system, we can contruct a dimensionless coupling constant g given by the equation *

$$g^2 = C^2 \left(\frac{m_0}{\hbar^3\omega^2}\right)^{\frac{1}{2}} = \frac{2\pi e^2}{\hbar c}\left(\frac{m_0}{\hbar\omega}\right)^{\frac{1}{2}}. \quad (5.322)$$

If g^2 is large compared to unity we have a case where strong coupling theories can be used, and if g^2 is small compared to unity, weak coupling theories apply. For most alkali halides c is of the order of magnitude 5, ω about 10^{13} to 10^{14} sec^{-1}, and $g(m/m_0)^{\frac{1}{4}} \sim 50$ (see Tiablikov 1953), where m is the free electron mass. The Russian group (Pekar, Bogoliubov, Tiablikov, and co-workers; for an account see Pekar 1954, 1956) assumed m_0 to be sufficiently larger than m to be able to use strong coupling theories, while Fröhlich and his co-workers (see Fröhlich 1954) have used the weak coupling approach. As in so many cases in physics, it turns out that in practical cases g is neither large nor small compared to unity, and the intermediate case is the most important one. This one has been studied by Höhler (1955a, b, 1956a, b) Feynman (1955a) and Schultz (1956).

We can now study some of the consequences of the Hamiltonian given in equation 5.321. From the canonical equations of motion we get

$$\dot{\mathbf{p}}' = 0, \quad \dot{\mathbf{x}}' = (\mathbf{p}' - \sum \mathbf{k}\,\alpha_{\mathbf{k}}\beta_{\mathbf{k}})/m_0, \quad (5.323)$$

$$\dot{\alpha}_{\mathbf{k}} = -i\left\{\frac{C}{k} + \alpha_{\mathbf{k}}\left[\omega - \frac{(\mathbf{k}\cdot\mathbf{p}' - \sum \mathbf{k}'\,\alpha_{\mathbf{k}'}\beta_{\mathbf{k}'})}{m_0}\right]\right\}, \quad (5.324)$$

* Note that c is *not* the velocity of light.

$$\dot{\beta}_{\mathbf{k}} = i\left\{\frac{C}{k} + \beta_{\mathbf{k}}\left[\omega - \frac{(\mathbf{k}\cdot\mathbf{p}' - \sum\mathbf{k}'\,\alpha_{\mathbf{k}'}\,\beta_{\mathbf{k}'})}{m_0}\right]\right\}. \quad (5.325)$$

These simultaneous nonlinear equations are difficult to solve. However, we can find a solution corresponding to the uniform motion of the electron and constant values of $\alpha_{\mathbf{k}}$ and $\beta_{\mathbf{k}}$. These constant values are given by the equation

$$\alpha_{\mathbf{k}} = \beta_{\mathbf{k}} = \frac{m_0 C}{k}[m_0\,\omega - (\mathbf{k}\cdot\mathbf{p}' - \sum\mathbf{k}'\,\alpha_{\mathbf{k}'}\,\beta_{\mathbf{k}'})]^{-1}. \quad (5.326)$$

As there is only one preferred direction in our system $(\mathbf{p}'/|\mathbf{p}'|)$, we can write

$$\sum\mathbf{k}'\,\alpha_{\mathbf{k}'}\,\beta_{\mathbf{k}'} = \eta\cdot\mathbf{p}', \quad (5.327)$$

and from equations 5.326 and 5.327 we get for η the implicit equation

$$\eta = \sum\frac{(\mathbf{k}\cdot\mathbf{p}')}{p'^2}\left(\frac{m_0 C}{k}\right)^2[m_0\,\omega - (\mathbf{k}\cdot\mathbf{p}')(1-\eta)]^{-2}. \quad (5.328)$$

If we consider slow moving electrons we can expand the expression in square brackets in powers of $(\mathbf{k}\cdot\mathbf{p}')$, and retaining only the first nonzero term we get for η the expression

$$\eta = \frac{A}{1+A}, \quad A = 2\sum_{\mathbf{k}}\frac{(\mathbf{k}\cdot\mathbf{p}')^2}{m_0\,\omega}\left(\frac{C}{kp'\,\omega}\right)^2. \quad (5.329)$$

The energy of the system is obtained by substituting expression 5.326 into equation 5.321 and using equations 5.327 and 5.328. The result is

$$E_{\text{pol}} = -\frac{C^2}{\omega}\sum_{\mathbf{k}}\frac{1}{k^2} + \frac{p'^2(1-\eta)}{2m_0}. \quad (5.330)$$

From equations 5.329 and 5.330 we see that it is necessary to introduce a cut-off wave number k_0, which means that our description of a polarizable medium breaks down for wave lengths which are too short. Using this cut-off, comparing equation 5.301 with equation 5.330, and using equation 5.329, we get for the polaron self-energy and effective mass the equations

$$E_0 = - 4\pi C^2 k_0/\omega, \qquad (5.331)$$

$$m_{\text{pol}} = m_0 (1 + A), \quad A = \frac{8\pi C^2 k_0^3}{9 m_0 \omega^3}. \qquad (5.332)$$

Let us now consider the limits of strong and weak coupling. In the case of strong coupling the cut-off will be given by the Debye cut-off, which means that k_0 will be independent of the coupling, and from equations 5.331 and 5.332 we find that E_0 and A are proportional to g^2, and m_{pol} practically equal to m_0. In the limit of weak coupling the cut-off will correspond to the de Broglie wave length of an electron with energy $\hbar\omega$,

$$k_0 = (2m_0 \omega/\hbar)^{\frac{1}{2}}, \qquad (5.333)$$

and now E_0 will be proportional to g, and A (and m_{pol}) to g^4.

We do not have the space to discuss any other aspects of the polaron here, but must refer to the survey papers mentioned earlier. However, we want to mention briefly the influence of the polarizable medium on excitons. One aspect of this problem was mentioned in the previous section, namely the mean free path of excitons, which is determined by the interaction between the exciton and the lattice vibrations. However, under certain circumstances the lattice can produce a polarization cloud which will accompany the exciton. It is necessary that the effective masses of the hole and of the electron be different, since otherwise the exciton will always present an essentially neutral entity to the polarizable medium. The theory of the so-called excitaron can be developed along the same lines as that of the polaron (Meyer 1956a, b; Haken 1957). An interesting new phenomenon is the possibility of the annihilation of an excitaron with the simultaneous emission of a number of phonons.

PART II

Theories of Collective Behaviour

CHAPTER 6

General Methods

In this chapter we shall discuss several general methods which have been devised to deal with systems showing collective behaviour. We shall pay special attention to the method developed by Tomonaga (1955a, b), as it is able to cover a large number of cases, some of which are discussed in Chapters 7 to 10. However, there are other methods which are perhaps not applicable quite as generally as Tomonaga's, and we shall discuss some of these in the present chapter as well as some of their applications in later chapters.

Most theories of collective behaviour start from a knowledge of the kind of collective motion to be expected — very often longitudinal waves. A particularly simple kind of collective motion is the motion of the centre of mass. We shall illustrate some of the methods discussed by showing how they can deal with centre-of-mass motion, but we shall see that some methods are essentially constructed for a very special choice of collective motion.

In the first section we discuss Tomonaga's general method and also briefly a method developed by Skinner (1956). In the next section we discuss the important special case of longitudinal waves, that is, the case where the Fourier components of the density are used as collective coordinates. Section 3 discusses the work of Yevick and Percus, and Section 4 discusses methods involving more variables than there are degrees of freedom. These include the methods of Zubarev and of Bohm and Pines. In all these sections we have developed the classical theory, although many of the original papers give only the quantum mechanical theory. This is done because in many ways the classical discussion is simpler and, moreover, the transition from classical to quantum mechanical language is usually easier to find than the other way around.

The last section deals with Skyrme's idea of considering sets of eigenstates which all have approximately the same internal motion though showing the whole gamut of collective motion.

The methods discussed are not applied to any particular cases in the present chapter. These applications will be discussed in the following chapters. Chapter 7 will deal with sound waves, Chapter 8 with electron plasmas, Chapter 9 with nuclear collective behaviour, and Chapter 10 with liquid helium.

6.1 Tomonaga's Method

In 1955 Tomonaga (1955a, b) presented a general method for discussing quantum mechanical collective motion. For most applications it is not necessary to use quantum mechanics, and we shall present his theory in classical form, indicating how it can be quantized.

We assume that the system can perform a collective motion which can be described by a potential function $\phi(\mathbf{x})$, that is, a motion corresponding to a displacement $\delta\mathbf{x}_i$ of the ith particle in the system given by the equation

$$\delta\mathbf{x}_i = \varepsilon\boldsymbol{\nabla}_i\,\phi(\mathbf{x}_i). \qquad (6.101)$$

Here ε measures the strength (or amplitude) of the collective motion. Our problem is to find a coordinate ξ and a canonically conjugate momentum π which will describe the collective motion. We shall discuss presently a few of the conditions which ξ and π must satisfy.

It is relatively simple to find π by reminding ourselves of the fact that any function $f(\mathbf{x}_i)$ which depends on the positions of the particles in the system will change its value from f to $f + \delta f$ when the particles are displaced according to equation 6.101 in such a way that

$$\delta f = \varepsilon\{f, \pi\}, \qquad (6.102)$$

provided we only consider infinitesimal displacements. In equation 6.102 $\{a, b\}$ denotes the Poisson bracket of a and b,

$$\{a, b\} = \sum_i \left(\frac{\partial a}{\partial q_i} \frac{\partial b}{\partial p_i} - \frac{\partial a}{\partial p_i} \frac{\partial b}{\partial q_i} \right), \qquad (6.103)$$

where the $q_i(p_i)$ are the $3N$ generalized coordinates (momenta) describing the systems of N particles. In our case we can use for the q_i the N $\mathbf{x}_i$ and for the p_i the N linear momentum vectors $\mathbf{p}_i$.

As we have for δf also the relation

$$\delta f = \sum_i(\delta\mathbf{x}_i \cdot \mathbf{\nabla}_i f) = \varepsilon \sum_i (\mathbf{\nabla}_i \phi \cdot \mathbf{\nabla}_i f), \qquad (6.104)$$

we find that if π is given by the equation

$$\pi = \sum_i(\mathbf{p}_i \cdot \mathbf{\nabla}_i \phi), \qquad (6.105)$$

equation 6.102 is satisfied.

Having found π, we now must determine ξ. If we were not concerned with constructing a theory which could be used to obtain results applicable to physical systems, there would be only one condition on ξ, namely,

$$\{\xi, \pi\} = 1. \qquad (6.106)$$

However, the reason for introducing special coordinates describing collective motion was to separate the collective motion from the internal (or particle) motion. Let η be an internal coordinate. We then know that η and π will satisfy the equation

$$\{\eta, \pi\} = 0, \quad \text{or,} \quad \sum_i(\mathbf{\nabla}_i \phi \cdot \mathbf{\nabla}_i \eta) = 0. \qquad (6.107)$$

If a separation is to be effected we must at least require that the kinetic energy expressed in π and the momentum (π_η) conjugate to η does not contain a cross term $\pi \cdot \pi_\eta$. This means that the surfaces $\xi = $ constant and $\eta = $ constant must be orthogonal onto each other, or, that

$$\sum_i (\boldsymbol{\nabla}_i \xi \cdot \boldsymbol{\nabla}_i \eta) = 0. \qquad (6.108)$$

In general it is not possible to find a ξ which satisfies both equation 6.106 and equation 6.108. There are two different ways to proceed from here. Brenig (1956) chooses ξ so as to satisfy equation 6.106 exactly and equation 6.108 approximately, while Tomonaga satisfies equation 6.108 exactly, and equation 6.106 approximately. We refer to Chapter 10 for a discussion of Brenig's method and shall use here Tomonaga's approach.

The similarity of equations 6.107 and 6.108 suggests for ξ the expression

$$\xi = A^{-1} \sum_i \phi(\mathbf{x}_i), \qquad (6.109)$$

where A is a constant. If we make this choice, equation 6.108 is satisfied automatically by virtue of equation 6.107. The constant A in equation 6.109 is still at our disposal to choose so as to satisfy equation 6.106 as well as possible.

We find that

$$\{\xi, \pi\} = A^{-1} \sum_i (\boldsymbol{\nabla}_i \phi \cdot \boldsymbol{\nabla}_i \phi). \qquad (6.110)$$

From the theory of probability it follows that usually, if we consider sums of the kind $F = \sum_i f(\mathbf{x}_i)$, the expression $[(F^2)_{\mathrm{av}} - (F_{\mathrm{av}})^2]/(F_{\mathrm{av}})^2$ will be of the order of magnitude N^{-1}, where N is the number of terms in the sum. Using this result and assuming that the physical systems under consideration are nonpathological, we can expect that $\sum_i (\boldsymbol{\nabla}_i \phi \cdot \boldsymbol{\nabla}_i \phi)$ will be equal to its mean value $[\sum_i (\boldsymbol{\nabla}_i \phi \cdot \boldsymbol{\nabla}_i \phi)]_{\mathrm{Av}}$ as long as we may neglect terms of the order $N^{-1/2}$. We have used the subscript "Av" to indicate the average over all possible physical configurations in coordinate space. We refer to Tomonaga's paper (1955a) for a discussion of this result. Accepting it, we see that we can satisfy equation 6.106 up to terms of the order $N^{-1/2}$, if we choose A to satisfy the equation

$$A = [\sum_i (\boldsymbol{\nabla}_i \phi \cdot \boldsymbol{\nabla}_i \phi)]_{\mathrm{Av}}. \qquad (6.111)$$

Before we show how we can express the Hamiltonian in terms of ξ and π, it is of some interest to consider the case where ϕ is a complex function, as will happen in the discussion of longitudinal waves. All quantities will now be complex. Equation 6.105 will still be valid, but instead of equation 6.108 we now have

$$\sum_i(\mathbf{\nabla}_i\xi^* \cdot \mathbf{\nabla}_i\eta) = 0, \qquad (6.112)$$

where an asterisk indicates the conjugate complex. Similarly we must make changes in equations 6.109, 6.110, and 6.111, and we have for ξ the equation

$$\xi = A^{-1}\sum_i\phi^*(\mathbf{x}_i), \quad A = [\sum_i\mathbf{\nabla}_i\phi^* \cdot \mathbf{\nabla}_i\phi)]_{Av} \qquad (6.113)$$

If ϕ is complex, we are dealing with two degrees of freedom of collective character, characterized by ξ, π and ξ^*, π^*.

We must now consider the Hamiltonian H of our system, which is given by the equation

$$H = T + U, \quad T = \sum_i(\mathbf{p}_i{}^2/2m), \qquad (6.114)$$

where we have assumed that we are dealing with only one kind of particle of mass m, and where T and U are the kinetic and potential energy.

Our next step is to split the kinetic energy into two parts, T_c and T_{in}, corresponding to the collective motion described by ξ and to the other degrees of freedom. From general principles one would expect T_c to be quadratic in π, or,

$$T_c = \pi^2/2I, \qquad (6.115)$$

where I represents the inertia of the collective mode. The constant I is determined by requiring T_{in} to be independent of π, which means that I is chosen in such a way that the following equation holds,

$$\{\xi, \ T_{in}\} = \{\xi, \ T - T_c\} = 0. \qquad (6.116)$$

Combining equations 6.116, 6.114, 6.115, 6.109, 6.106, and

6.105 we find that

$$I = mA. \tag{6.117}$$

We must emphasize at this point that inasmuch as equation 6.106 is only approximately valid, the separation of the collective mode from the other degrees of freedom is only approximate.

We have now found a T_{in} which does not contain π, but it may still contain ξ and, in general, U will also contain ξ. The next step will be to express $T_{\text{in}} + U$ in terms of ξ. This will in general be very complicated, but in many cases one may assume that the amplitude of the collective motion is so small that one can use a power series expansion in ξ, stopping at the term in ξ^2. Tomonaga developed a very pretty trick to obtain this series expansion. The background of his trick is that, if we want to use a Taylor expansion for U, say, we must know $U(0)$, $U'(0)$, $U''(0), \ldots$, where the primes indicate differentiation with respect to ξ and the 0 the fact that we take those functions at $\xi = 0$. However, we only know $U(\xi)$, and we can obtain $U'(\xi)$, $U''(\xi), \ldots$ by using Poisson brackets,

$$U'(\xi) = \{U, \pi\}, \ U''(\xi) = \{\{U, \pi\}, \pi\}. \tag{6.118}$$

We can now use for $U(0)$, $U'(0), \ldots$ Taylor expansions of the kind

$$U(0) = U(\xi) - \xi U'(\xi) + \tfrac{1}{2}\xi^2 U''(\xi) - \ldots. \tag{6.119}$$

If we want $U(\xi)$ only up to terms of order ξ^2 we use the identity

$$U(\xi) = [U(\xi) - \xi U'(\xi) + \tfrac{1}{2}\xi^2 U''(\xi)] \\ + [U'(\xi) - \xi U''(\xi)]\xi + [\tfrac{1}{2}U''(\xi)]\xi^2, \tag{6.120}$$

where the coefficients inside the square brackets are independent of ξ up to terms of the order $\xi^2(\xi, \xi^0)$. We may draw attention to the fact that the coefficients inside the square brackets are functions of the original coordinates $\mathbf{x}_i$, since $U(\xi)$ is expressed in the $\mathbf{x}_i$, and $U'(\xi)$, $U''(\xi), \ldots$ also, if we use equations 6.118 and 6.105.

A similar procedure can be adopted for $T_{in}(\xi)$, and the final result for H is

$$H = [T_{in}^{(0)} + U^{(0)}] + [T_{in}^{(1)} + U^{(1)}]\,\xi$$
$$+ [T_{in}^{(2)} + U^{(2)}]\,\xi^2 + \pi^2/2mA, \quad (6.121)$$

in an easily understandable notation.

In general the expressions within the square brackets will still contain the particle coordinates. In order that the expression of equation 6.121 be useful it is necessary, first of all, that the coefficient of ξ^2 does not contain the particle coordinates any longer, so that the collective Hamiltonian, H_c, given by the equation

$$H_c = T_c + U_c = (\pi^2/2mA) + [T_{in}^{(2)} + U^{(2)}]\xi^2, \quad (6.122)$$

depends on ξ and π only. Secondly, it is necessary that the interaction term $[T_{in}^{(1)} + U^{(1)}]\xi$ is sufficiently small to be negligible. If those two conditions are satisfied, it will only be the particle Hamiltonian, H_p, given by the equation

$$H_p = T_{in}^{(0)} + U^{(0)}, \quad (6.123)$$

which will govern the particle (internal) degrees of freedom. We must emphasize that $U^{(0)}$ differs, in general, from U. In the case of longitudinal plasma waves, for instance, $U^{(0)}$ contains only short range, screened Coulomb interactions; the long range interactions are taken into account in the collective modes.

The transition to quantum mechanics is simple and straightforward. Everywhere we replace the Poisson brackets by the corresponding commutators according to the equation

$$\{a, b\} \to [a, b]_-/i\hbar, \quad [a, b]_- = ab - ba. \quad (6.124)$$

Let us finally see how Tomonaga's method can be applied to the centre-of-mass motion. In this case the three components of the centre-of-mass motion correspond to the following three potential functions ϕ,

$$\phi_1(\mathbf{x}) = x, \; \phi_2(\mathbf{x}) = y, \quad \phi_3(\mathbf{x}) = z, \quad (6.125)$$

and equations 6.105, 6.109, and 6.111 lead to

$$\pi_1 = \sum_i p_{xi}, \ \pi_2 = \sum_i p_{yi}, \ \pi_3 = \sum_i p_{zi}, \qquad (6.126)$$

and

$$\xi_1 = A^{-1}\sum_i x_i, \ \xi_2 = A^{-1}\sum_i y_i, \ \xi_3 = A^{-1}\sum_i z_i, \ A = N, \quad (6.127)$$

while in this particular case equation 6.106 is exactly satisfied. The π_k and ξ_k are the components of the total linear momentum and of the position of the centre of mass, as would be expected. The quantity I given by equation 6.127 is the total mass of the system, again as was to be expected.

It must be emphasized that Tomonaga's method is mainly applicable when one is interested in the collective modes only, and does not want to consider the particle modes at the same time. If there are altogether n collective degrees of freedom, Tomonaga's method implies that it is possible to find $3N - n$ particle coordinates η_j apart from the n collective coordinates ξ_k. To that extent the problem of redundant variables (see Section 4) does not enter into this discussion. In Chapter 10, however, where we are interested in the particle coordinates we shall see one way of how one might tackle this problem. Another method for attacking this difficulty has been developed by Skinner (1956) who has, however, not yet applied his method to any physical problem except the centre-of-mass motion. It is difficult to see whether his method can be applied to other problems, and it seems doubtful whether it would be an improvement over Tomonaga's method. In the quantum mechanical case it has some similarity to Brenig's method (1956) in that use is made of delta-functions to reduce the number of degrees of freedom to $3N$ (compare the discussion in Chapter 10). We shall briefly sketch Skinner's theory and outline its application to the centre-of-mass motion, restricting ourselves to a classical description. We must refer to the original paper for details.

Let us consider a system of N identical particles with

position coordinates x_i $(i = 1, \ldots, 3N)$ and let p_i $(i = 1, \ldots, 3N)$ be the corresponding momenta, obtained in the usual way from the Lagrangian of the system (see, for instance, Goldstein 1950, p. 48). We want to describe this system by a set of n collective coordinates ξ_k and some particle coordinates η_i. As in the original equations of motion the laboratory coordinates x_i entered symmetrically, we should like to find a set of η_i which are symmetrical too. It would, of course, be advantageous to use for the η_i the x_i, but in that case we would have landed ourselves with $3N + n$ coordinates to describe our system which has only $3N$ degrees of freedom. We remind ourselves that the collective modes involve, of course, the x_i, that is, that there are n relations of the kind

$$\xi_k = f_k(x_i). \qquad (6.128)$$

Secondly, we remember that the η_i should describe the behaviour of the system, once the collective modes have been taken into account, which means that they are the laboratory coordinates provided there is no collective motion, or, we can use for the η_i the x_i with the n constraints (compare the discussion in Section 6.4)

$$\xi_k = 0, \quad \text{or,} \quad f_k(\eta_i) = 0. \qquad (6.129)$$

This method has the advantage of giving a prescription how to get the η_i. The next problem is to find the transformation from the x_i to the ξ_k and η_i, that is, a one-to-one transformation connecting the $3N$-dimensional subspace of the $3N + n$-dimensional ξ, η-space satisfying the constraints of equation 6.129 with the $3N$-dimensional x-space. This is done by extending x-space to $3N + n$ dimensions through the introduction of n extra coordinates x_j $(j = 3N + 1, \ldots, 3N + n)$ which are related to the η_i by the equations

$$x_j = f_k(\eta_i), \ j = k + 3N, \ k = 1, \ldots, n, \qquad (6.130)$$

and which are required to be identically equal to zero. We can now transform from the $3N + n$-dimensional x-space

to the $3N + n$-dimensional ξ, η-space, and the constraints
of equation 6.129 define both the subspace in ξ, η-space
corresponding to possible configurations of the system and
the subspace in x-space corresponding to all $x_j = 0$ $(j > 3N)$.

In order to get the equations of motion in canonical
form we should like to construct a Hamiltonian H in the
usual manner from the Lagrangian L,

$$H = \sum_\xi \dot{\xi}\,\pi_\xi + \sum_\eta \dot{\eta}\,\pi_\eta - L(\dot{\xi},\ \dot{\eta},\ \xi,\ \eta), \qquad (6.131)$$

where the momenta π_ξ and π_η are defined in the usual way,

$$\pi_\xi = \partial L/\partial \dot{\xi}, \quad \pi_\eta = \partial L/\partial \dot{\eta}. \qquad (6.132)$$

We get $L(\dot{\xi},\ \dot{\eta},\ \xi,\ \eta)$ from $L(\dot{x}_i,\ x_i)$ using the transformations

$$x_i = x_i(\xi, \eta),\ i = 1, \ldots, 3N;$$
$$x_j = f_k(\eta),\ j = k + 3N, \quad k = 1, \ldots, n, \quad (6.133)$$

and

$$\dot{x}_i = \sum_\xi \frac{\partial x_i}{\partial \xi}\,\dot{\xi} + \sum_\eta \frac{\partial x_i}{\partial \eta}\,\dot{\eta}, \quad \dot{x}_j = \sum_\eta \frac{\partial f_{j-3N}}{\partial \eta}\,\dot{\eta}. \quad (6.134)$$

The equations of motion follow then in the usual way from
the equation

$$\dot{F} = \{F,\ H\}. \qquad (6.135)$$

We must draw attention to the fact that the π_ξ and π_η
are not necessarily momenta canonically conjugate to ξ
and η for our original system. The reason is that we have
$3N + n$ coordinates describing a system of $3N$ degrees of
freedom. Skinner shows how one can choose the η_i in such
a way that at least the Poisson bracket of any ξ or π_ξ with
any other ξ, π_ξ, η, or π_η, vanishes except the Poisson bracket
$\{\xi,\ \pi_\xi\}$, where ξ and π_ξ correspond to each other in which
case $\{\xi,\ \pi_\xi\} = 1$.

Let us consider now the centre-of-mass motion, and to
simplify the discussion, let us restrict ourselves to a one-
dimensional system of particles of mass m. The $\eta_1, \ldots, \eta_N$
are now the relative coordinates, and the ξ is the centre-of-

mass coordinate. Equations 6.128, 6.129, and 6.133 are now of the form

$$N\xi = \sum_i x_i, \qquad (6.136)$$

$$\sum_i \eta_i = 0, \qquad (6.137)$$

$$x_i = \xi + \eta_i, \; i = 1, \ldots, N; \; x_{N+1} = \sum_i \eta_i. \quad (6.138)$$

The Lagrangian L will be of the form

$$L = \tfrac{1}{2}m\sum_i \dot{x}_i^2 - \sum_{i \neq j} U(x_i - x_j), \qquad (6.139)$$

and we get from equations 6.134 and 6.132

$$\dot{x}_i = \dot{\xi} + \dot{\eta}_i, \; i = 1, \ldots, N; \; \dot{x}_{N+1} = \sum_i \dot{\eta}_i, \quad (6.140)$$

$$\pi_\xi = m \sum_i(\dot{\xi} + \dot{\eta}_i), \; \pi_{\eta i} = m(\dot{\xi} + \dot{\eta}_i), \qquad (6.141)$$

so that the Hamiltonian is of the form

$$H = \frac{\pi_\xi^2}{2mN} + \sum_i \frac{\pi_{\eta i}^2}{2m} - \frac{(\sum_i \pi_{\eta i})^2}{2mN} + \sum_{i \neq j} U(\eta_i - \eta_j). \quad (6.142)$$

If one introduces new η'_i in such a way that

$$\pi'_{\eta i} = \pi_{\eta i} - (\sum_j \pi_{\eta j}/N), \qquad (6.143)$$

the Hamiltonian will be of the simple form

$$H = \sum_i \frac{\pi_{\eta i}'^2}{2m} + \frac{\pi_\xi^2}{2mN} + \sum_{i \neq j} U(\eta_i - \eta_j). \quad (6.144)$$

Although Skinner's method gives a clear prescription for obtaining the Hamiltonian in terms of collective coordinates, it seems difficult to estimate the errors involved in the separation of the ξ's and the η's (these enter because we treat by canonical methods a system which is not truly canonical) and also it seems difficult to extend his procedure beyond the case of the centre-of-mass motion, as it involves expressing the original laboratory coordinates in terms of the ξ's and η's.

6.2   Fourier Components of the Density as Collective Coordinates

In many systems there can occur longitudinal waves, and it is of some interest to discuss the general case of such longitudinal waves in some detail before we apply the theory to some particular problems. In fact, they are the collective coordinates which have been most widely — and often exclusively — used (Zubarev 1953, 1954, Bohm and Pines 1953, Pines and Bohm 1952, Pines 1953, Yevick and Percus 1956, Percus and Yevick 1956, 1957a, b, c, d, e, Brenig 1956, Bogoliubov and Zubarev 1955, Galasiewicz 1955, 1956a, b). We shall discuss in this section how these waves can be treated using Tomonaga's method and after that, in Section 6.3, we shall discuss some of the aspects discussed by Yevick and Percus.

The generating function for a longitudinal wave of wave vector $\mathbf{k}$ is given by either of the following two functions

$$\phi_{\pm\mathbf{k}}(\mathbf{x}) = k^{-1} \exp\left[\pm i(\mathbf{k} \cdot \mathbf{x})\right], \qquad (6.201)$$

where k is the absolute magnitude of $\mathbf{k}$. Using equations 6.105 and 6.113 we get

$$\pi_{\pm\mathbf{k}} = \pm\, ik^{-1} \sum_j (\mathbf{k} \cdot \mathbf{p}_j) \exp\left[\pm i(\mathbf{k} \cdot \mathbf{x}_j)\right], \qquad (6.202)$$

$$A = N, \qquad (6.203)$$

$$\xi_{\pm\mathbf{k}} = (Nk)^{-1} \sum_j \exp\left[\mp i(\mathbf{k} \cdot \mathbf{x}_j)\right]. \qquad (6.204)$$

If $\rho(\mathbf{x})$ is the density of the system, we can write

$$\rho(\mathbf{x}) = m \sum_j \delta(\mathbf{x} - \mathbf{x}_j), \qquad (6.205)$$

where $\delta(\mathbf{x})$ is the three-dimensional delta function, and if we denote the Fourier components of the density by $\rho_{\mathbf{k}}$, we have

$$\rho_{\mathbf{k}} = V^{-1}\!\int\!\rho(\mathbf{x})\exp\left[-i(\mathbf{k}\cdot\mathbf{x})\right] d^3\mathbf{x} = (m/V) \sum_j \exp\left[-i(\mathbf{k}\cdot\mathbf{x}_j)\right], \qquad (6.206)$$

where V is the volume of the system. We note that, apart from a multiplying constant the $\xi_{\mathbf{k}}$ are the Fourier components of the density.

Let us for the moment restrict ourselves to only one wave vector $\mathbf{k}$. We notice first of all that equation 6.106 is exactly satisfied and not just only approximately. Evaluating all possible Poisson brackets we have

$$\{\xi_{+\mathbf{k}}, \pi_{+\mathbf{k}}\} = \{\xi_{-\mathbf{k}}, \pi_{-\mathbf{k}}\} = 1, \quad \{\xi_{+\mathbf{k}}, \xi_{-\mathbf{k}}\} = 0, \tag{6.207}$$

$$\{\pi_{+\mathbf{k}}, \pi_{-\mathbf{k}}\} = 2i \sum_j (\mathbf{p}_j \cdot \mathbf{k}), \{\xi_{+\mathbf{k}}, \pi_{-\mathbf{k}}\} = \{\xi_{-\mathbf{k}}, \pi_{+\mathbf{k}}\}^* $$
$$= - N^{-1} \sum_j \exp\left[- 2i(\mathbf{k} \cdot \mathbf{x}_j)\right]. \tag{6.208}$$

We shall assume that we are working in the centre-of-mass frame of reference so that $\{\pi_{+\mathbf{k}}, \pi_{-\mathbf{k}}\} = 0$. If $\xi_{\pm\mathbf{k}}$ and $\pi_{\pm\mathbf{k}}$ are to be suitable canonical coordinates we must have vanishing Poisson brackets $\{\xi_{+\mathbf{k}}, \pi_{-\mathbf{k}}\}$ and $\{\xi_{-\mathbf{k}}, \pi_{+\mathbf{k}}\}$. We see that these Poisson brackets do not vanish exactly. Let us, however, consider for a moment sums of the type

$$S_{\mathbf{k}} = \sum_j \exp i(\mathbf{k} \cdot \mathbf{x}_j), \tag{6.209}$$

which will play an important part in our discussion. We note, for instance, that they are identical with $\xi_{-\mathbf{k}}$ apart from a multiplying factor. In Appendix A it is shown that their mean value is zero with a mean deviation of the order of $N^{\frac{1}{2}}$, provided we may use the so-called *random phase approximation*.

We see that $\{\xi_{+\mathbf{k}}, \pi_{-\mathbf{k}}\}$ and $\{\xi_{-\mathbf{k}}, \pi_{+\mathbf{k}}\}^*$ are equal to $- k\xi_{2\mathbf{k}}$, that is, to $- S_{-2\mathbf{k}}/N$, or, of the order $N^{-\frac{1}{2}}$, if we can trust the random phase approximation. We shall assume that we may trust the results obtained in that way and, generally speaking, we shall neglect terms of relative order $N^{-\frac{1}{2}}$. Under those circumstances $\xi_{\pm\mathbf{k}}$ and $\pi_{\pm\mathbf{k}}$ form a suitable set of canonical coordinates.

We must first of all find the collective kinetic energy which will now be of the form

$$T_{\mathbf{c}} = A\pi_{+\mathbf{k}}^2 + B\pi_{+\mathbf{k}}\,\pi_{-\mathbf{k}} + C\pi_{-\mathbf{k}}^2. \tag{6.210}$$

Using the same methods as those employed in deriving equation 6.117 we find

$$A = C = 0, \quad B = (Nm)^{-1}. \qquad (6.211)$$

The other terms in the Hamiltonian are now also more complicated as they contain Poisson brackets involving both $\pi_{+\mathbf{k}}$ and $\pi_{-\mathbf{k}}$. We shall first evaluate T_{1n} which is now given by the equation

$$T_{1n} = \sum_j (\mathbf{p}_j^2/2m) - (Nmk^2)^{-1} | \sum_j (\mathbf{k} \cdot \mathbf{p}_j) \exp i(\mathbf{k} \cdot \mathbf{x}_j)|^2. \quad (6.212)$$

The relevant Poisson brackets are

$$\{T_{1n}, \pi_{\pm\mathbf{k}}\} = (mk)^{-1} \sum_j (\mathbf{k} \cdot \mathbf{p}_j)^2 \exp [\pm i(\mathbf{k} \cdot \mathbf{x}_j)], \qquad (6.213)$$

$$\{\{T_{1n}, \pi_{\pm\mathbf{k}}\}, \pi_{\pm\mathbf{k}}\} = m^{-1} \sum_j (\mathbf{k} \cdot \mathbf{p}_j)^2 \exp [\pm 2i(\mathbf{k} \cdot \mathbf{x}_j)], \quad (6.214)$$

$$\{\{T_{1n}, \pi_{\pm\mathbf{k}}\}, \pi_{\mp\mathbf{k}}\} = 3m^{-1} \sum_j (\mathbf{k} \cdot \mathbf{p}_j)^2. \qquad (6.215)$$

If we can use the random phase approximation, the Poisson brackets of equations 6.213 and 6.214 are of order $N^{-\frac{1}{2}}$ compared to those of equations 6.215 and in that approximation can be put equal to zero.

As far as the potential energy is concerned, we shall for the moment assume that it can be written in the form

$$U = \tfrac{1}{2} \sum_{j \neq n} U_{jn}(\mathbf{x}_j - \mathbf{x}_n), \qquad (6.216)$$

that is, we assume additivity and two-body forces. Moreover, we shall assume that the forces are central forces so that

$$U = \tfrac{1}{2} \sum_{j \neq n} U(r_{jn}), \qquad (6.217)$$

where r_{jn} is the distance apart of the jth and the nth particle, and where $U(r)$ is the interparticle potential. The Fourier transform of $U(\mathbf{x})$ will be denoted by $U_{\mathbf{k}}$,

$$U(\mathbf{x}) = \sum_{\mathbf{k}} U_{\mathbf{k}} \exp i(\mathbf{k} \cdot \mathbf{x}), \qquad (6.218)$$

and because we are dealing with central forces, $U_{\mathbf{k}}$ will depend on k only, which we shall indicate by writing $U(k)$ instead of $U_{\mathbf{k}}$.

We must now evaluate the Poisson brackets involving U. They have the following values:

$$\{U, \pi_{\pm\mathbf{k}}\} = NkU(k) \sum_j \exp\left[\pm i(\mathbf{k} \cdot \mathbf{x}_j)\right], \quad (6.219)$$

$$\{\{U, \pi_{\pm\mathbf{k}}\}, \pi_{\pm\mathbf{k}}\} = 0, \quad \{\{U, \pi_{\pm\mathbf{k}}\}, \pi_{\mp\mathbf{k}}\} = N^2 k^2 U(k). \quad (6.220)$$

In evaluating these Poisson brackets we have used the Fourier expansion of equation 6.218. Moreover, we have used the random phase approximation in neglecting in equations 6.219 and 6.220 terms of relative order $N^{-\frac{1}{2}}$. For instance, in deriving equation 6.219 we write

$$\{U, \pi_{-\mathbf{k}}\} = \sum_{j \neq n} \sum_{\mathbf{k}'} U_{\mathbf{k}'} \left[(\mathbf{k} \cdot \mathbf{k}')/k\right] \exp\{i(\mathbf{x}_n \cdot \mathbf{k}' - \mathbf{k}) - i(\mathbf{k}' \cdot \mathbf{x}_j)\}$$
$$= N \sum_j k U_{\mathbf{k}} \exp\left[-i(\mathbf{k} \cdot \mathbf{x}_j)\right]$$
$$+ \sum_{j \neq n} \sum_{\mathbf{k}'(\neq \mathbf{k})} \exp\left[-i(\mathbf{k}' \cdot \mathbf{x}_j) + i(\mathbf{x}_n \cdot \mathbf{k}' - \mathbf{k})\right]$$
$$\left[(\mathbf{k} \cdot \mathbf{k}') U_{\mathbf{k}'}/k\right]$$
$$= NkU(k) \sum_j \exp\left[-i(\mathbf{k} \cdot \mathbf{x}_j)\right] + \text{terms of order } N^{-\frac{1}{2}}.$$

We can now use for U an equation analogous to equation 6.120 and we have

$$U = U^0 + U^+ \xi_{+\mathbf{k}} + U^- \xi_{-\mathbf{k}} + U^{++} \xi_{+\mathbf{k}}^2 + U^{+-} \xi_{+\mathbf{k}} \xi_{-\mathbf{k}} + U^{--} \xi_{-\mathbf{k}}^2 \quad (6.221)$$

with

$$U^0 = \tfrac{1}{2} \sum_{j \neq n} U_0(r_{jn}), \quad U_0(r) = \sum_{\mathbf{k}'(\neq \pm \mathbf{k})} U(k') \exp i(\mathbf{k}' \cdot \mathbf{x}), \quad (6.222)$$

$$U^+ = U^- = U^{++} = U^{--} = 0, \quad U^{+-} = N^2 k^2 U(k), \quad (6.223)$$

or,

$$U = \tfrac{1}{2} \sum_{j \neq n} U_0(r_{jn}) + N^2 k^2 U(k) \xi_{+\mathbf{k}} \xi_{-\mathbf{k}}. \quad (6.224)$$

There are two points of interest here. First of all, although in deriving equations 6.222 and 6.223 we have neglected repeatedly terms of relative order $N^{-\frac{1}{2}}$, equation 6.224 is exact. However, the separation implied in that equation is approximate inasmuch as U^0 is independent of $\xi_{\pm\mathbf{k}}$ only to the extent that the terms neglected could, indeed, be neglected. Secondly, we note that $U_0(r)$ is $U(r)$, but for the omission of the two Fourier terms corresponding to the wave vectors of the collective coordinates.

In order to get the Hamiltonian we should now write down for T_{1n} an expression similar to the expression of equation 6.221. We shall assume that we may put T_{1n}^+ and T_{1n}^- equal to zero, an assumption which we shall briefly discuss presently. In that case we have for the Hamiltonian, as $T_{1n}^{++} = T_{1n}^{--} = 0$ in the usual approximation,

$$H = T_{1n}^0 + U^0 + [3m^{-1} \sum_j (\mathbf{k} \cdot \mathbf{p}_j)^2 + N^2 k^2 U(k)]\xi_{+\mathbf{k}} \, \xi_{-\mathbf{k}}$$
$$+ (Nm)^{-1} \pi_{+\mathbf{k}} \, \pi_{-\mathbf{k}}, \quad (6.225)$$

where we have used equations 6.210, 6.211, 6.215, 6.221, 6.222, and 6.223.

From the canonical equations of motion

$$\dot{\pi}_{\pm\mathbf{k}} = - \, \partial H/\partial \xi_{\pm\mathbf{k}}, \quad \dot{\xi}_{\pm\mathbf{k}} = \partial H/\partial \pi_{\pm\mathbf{k}}, \quad (6.226)$$

we get for $\xi_{\pm\mathbf{k}}$ a harmonic behaviour, $\xi_{\pm\mathbf{k}}(t) = \xi_{\pm\mathbf{k}}(0) \cdot \exp{(i\omega_{\mathbf{k}}t)}$ with a frequency $\omega_{\mathbf{k}}$ given by the equation,

$$\omega_{\mathbf{k}}^2 = 3(Nm^2)^{-1} \sum_j (\mathbf{k} \cdot \mathbf{p}_j)^2 + Nm^{-1}k^2 U(k). \quad (6.227)$$

Let us consider for a moment the neglect of the terms in T_{1n} linear in $\xi_{\pm\mathbf{k}}$. It is true to say that their coefficients are smaller than the coefficient of $\xi_{+\mathbf{k}} \, \xi_{-\mathbf{k}}$ by a factor of the order $N^{-\frac{1}{2}}$ and to that extent their neglect might be justified. However, as the $\xi_{\pm\mathbf{k}}$ themselves are quantities of the order of $N^{-\frac{1}{2}}$ the linear terms would give rise to contributions to the Hamiltonian of the same order of magnitude as the quadratic terms, and if one would consider situations where $\xi_{\pm\mathbf{k}}$ would no longer necessarily be small, there would also be no reason to assume that the coefficients of the linear terms were small. For the sake of convenience we shall neglect these terms. They describe the interaction between the collective modes and the particle modes and they should be studied. We may remark here that they are dropped in Bohm and Pines' work on plasma oscillations (see Chapter 8), that they vanish in the case of a one-dimensional degenerate Fermi gas (see Tomonaga 1955b, also ter Haar 1957), and that Percus and Yevick assume from the beginning that there are not going to be any linear terms.

Let us now consider the case where we introduce a number of collective coordinates corresponding to different wave vectors. The only new point of interest is the evaluation of the Poisson brackets corresponding to variables with different wave vectors. We find for the Poisson brackets the following values:

$$\{\xi_{\mathbf{k}}, \pi_{\mathbf{k}'}\} = (\mathbf{k} \cdot \mathbf{k}') S_{\mathbf{k}-\mathbf{k}'}/Nkk', \qquad (6.228)$$

$$\{\xi_{\mathbf{k}}, \xi_{\mathbf{k}'}\} = 0, \qquad (6.229)$$

$$\{\pi_{\mathbf{k}}, \pi_{\mathbf{k}'}\} = [i(\mathbf{k} \cdot \mathbf{k}')/kk'] \sum_j (\mathbf{p}_j \cdot \mathbf{k}' - \mathbf{k}) \exp[i(\mathbf{k} + \mathbf{k}' \cdot \mathbf{x}_j)]. \qquad (6.230)$$

If we assume again that we are working in the centre-of-mass system and that we may neglect terms of the order $N^{-\frac{1}{2}}$, we get for the Poisson brackets the proper expressions corresponding to a set of canonical variables,

$$\{\xi_{\mathbf{k}}, \xi_{\mathbf{k}'}\} = \{\pi_{\mathbf{k}}, \pi_{\mathbf{k}'}\} = 0, \quad \{\xi_{\mathbf{k}}, \pi_{\mathbf{k}'}\} = \delta_{\mathbf{k}\mathbf{k}'}, \quad (6.231)$$

where $\delta_{\mathbf{k}\mathbf{k}'}$ is the Kronegger symbol.

The Hamiltonian of the system is now given by the equation

$$H = T_{1n}^0 + U^0$$
$$+ \sum_{\mathbf{k}} \{[3m^{-1} \sum_j (\mathbf{k} \cdot \mathbf{p}_j)^2 + N^2 k^2 U(k)] \xi_{+\mathbf{k}} \xi_{-\mathbf{k}} + (Nm)^{-1} \pi_{+\mathbf{k}} \pi_{-\mathbf{k}}\}, \qquad (6.232)$$

to the same approximation as the one used to derive equation 6.223. The sum over $\mathbf{k}$ in equation 6.232 extends over all wave vectors corresponding to collective modes. If we denote the set of those wave vectors by $\{\mathbf{k}\}$ and the set of all other wave vectors by $\{\{\mathbf{k}\}\}$, U^0 is now given by the equation

$$U^0 = \tfrac{1}{2} \sum_{j \neq n} U_0(r_{jn}), \quad U_0(r) = \sum_{\{\{\mathbf{k}\}\}} U(k) \exp i(\mathbf{k} \cdot \mathbf{x}). \quad (6.233)$$

Equation 6.227 for $\omega_{\mathbf{k}}$ remains valid. It might be considered that $\omega_{\mathbf{k}}$ still contains a particle element in that it
contains a sum over all the particles. This is, of course,
true, but for many applications (see Chapters 7 and 8) we
can write

$$(Nm^2)^{-1} \sum_j (\mathbf{k} \cdot \mathbf{p}_j)^2 \doteq \tfrac{1}{3}k^2(Nm^2)^{-1} \sum_j \mathbf{p}_j{}^2 = \tfrac{2}{3}k^2m^{-1}\langle T \rangle, \quad (6.234)$$

where $\langle T \rangle$ is the average kinetic energy per particle which
we may put equal to $3/2k_{\mathrm{B}}T$ if we are dealing with a classical
system in temperature equilibrium.

6.3   Yevick and Percus' Method

Yevick and Percus (1956, Percus and Yevick 1956,
1957a, b, c, d, e) have developed a theory of many-body
systems using a set of N ξ_k as coordinates instead of the N
x_j. (Most of their considerations are of a one-dimensional
system, and we shall restrict our discussion to that case.)
Their idea is that just as careful consideration of the system,
using the x_j, will show up collective behaviour, so also
should a theory, using the ξ_k, show up particle behaviour
if carried sufficiently far. They use mainly a Lagrangian
approach, starting from the Lagrangian

$$L(x_j, \dot{x}_j) = \sum_j \tfrac{1}{2}m\dot{x}_j{}^2 - \tfrac{1}{2}\sum_{j \neq n}U(x_j - x_n). \quad (6.301)$$

In order that the ξ_k are convenient coordinates, it is important that, at any rate to a good approximation, the
Lagrangian in terms of the ξ_k, $\dot{\xi}_k$ will be of the form

$$L(\xi_k, \dot{\xi}_k) = \tfrac{1}{2}\sum_{\{k\}}[f_k\,\dot{\xi}_k\,\dot{\xi}_{-k} - \nu_k\,\xi_k\,\xi_{-k}] + A, \quad (6.302)$$

where $\{k\}$ denotes the complete set of N wave vectors k
used, and where A is a constant to be determined. The
coefficients f_k and ν_k also have to be determined. We note
that as ξ_k for $k = 0$ is not a suitable coordinate, the set
$\{k\}$ will not contain $k = 0$. We shall assume the system
to be enclosed in a "volume" L, so that all k of the set $\{k\}$
are integral multiples of the wave number k_0 given by the
equation

$$k_0 = 2\pi/L. \qquad (6.303)$$

Percus and Yevick have developed two different methods to obtain the values of the f_k and ν_k. The first method (Percus and Yevick 1956) they call mathematical or kinematical, and the second one (Percus and Yevick 1957a) physical or dynamical. They also show that the two methods lead to essentially the same results.

We do not want to discuss their methods in all detail, and shall restrict ourselves to a discussion of the determination of the ν_k, stating the results for the f_k and discussing some of the problems particular to the approximation of the terms with the $\dot{x}_j$ by the terms involving the $\dot{\xi}_k$.

Substituting the expression of equation 6.204 for ξ_k into $A - \frac{1}{2} \sum_{\{k\}} \nu_k \xi_k \xi_{-k}$ we find that it reduces to $-\frac{1}{2} \sum_{j \neq n} U(x_j - x_n)$, provided the following equations can be satisfied

$$2NA = -(N-1)B + \sum_{\{k\}} \nu_k/k^2, \qquad (6.304)$$

$$N^2 U(x_j - x_n) = B + \sum_{\{k\}} (\nu_k/k^2) \exp\left[ik(x_j - x_n)\right]. \qquad (6.305)$$

If the set $\{k\}$ were a complete set, equation 6.305 would be the Fourier expansion of $U(x_j - x_n)$. However, the set $\{k\}$ is not complete. Percus and Yevick show that it is possible to find a function $d(x)$ which can be represented by N Fourier components only, and which shows a delta-function-like behaviour. We have thus for $d(x)$ the expansion

$$d(x) = L^{-1}[d_0 + \sum_{\{k\}} d_k \exp\,(ikx)], \quad d_0 = 1. \qquad (6.306)$$

If $d(x)$ shows, indeed, delta-function-like behaviour, we have to a fair approximation — called hereafter the "d-approximation" — for any function $F(x)$,

$$\begin{aligned}
F(x) &\doteq \int F(x')d(x - x')dx \\
&= \sum_{\{k,0\}} (d_k/L)\left[\int F(x')(\exp\,(-ikx')dx'\right] \exp\,(ikx) \\
&= \sum_{\{k,0\}} d_k F_k \exp\,(ikx), \qquad (6.307)
\end{aligned}$$

where F_k denotes the Fourier components of $F(x)$, and where $\{k, 0\}$ denotes the set consisting of $\{k\}$ together with $k = 0$.

We see that in the "d-approximation" equation 6.305 can be satisfied by putting

$$B = U(0)N^2, \quad \nu_k = N^2 k^2 d_k U(k), \qquad (6.308)$$

and A is fixed by equation 6.304.

One finds similarly for the f_k the expressions

$$f_k = mN^2 d_k / \left[\sum_{\{k, 0\}} d_k \right]. \qquad (6.309)$$

There is, however, one difference between the potential energy terms and the kinetic energy terms. In the first case, the expressions in the ξ- and in the x-representation respectively are the same in the "d-approximation," but in the second case, even in the "d-approximation" there are still some terms left which occur only in one of the two representations, namely, essentially the following terms:

$$\sum_{j \neq n} d(x_j - x_n) \dot{x}_j \dot{x}_n \qquad (6.310)$$

Percus and Yevick discuss these terms and show that they will be small, provided one chooses a random distribution of the integers used to get the set $\{k\}$ (we do not wish to discuss here what is meant by the term "random" in this connexion). This entails that the d_k will not all be equal (compare equation 6.318 below). This, in turn, means that the natural choice $d_k = 1$ — which corresponds on the one hand to the Fourier components of the delta-function, and on the other hand to the Hamiltonian of equation 6.225 — is not a good one. It would be of interest to consider in more detail the extra terms occurring when one actually chooses $d_k = 1$, and to compare them to the terms in the kinetic energy linear in the ξ_k, which were neglected in the previous section.

We should like to discuss briefly the nature of the d-function. The requirements for its usefulness are, first of all, that an equation similar to equation 6.307 gives a satisfactory representation of the potential energy U and,

secondly, that terms of the kind of expression 6.310 are small
in general. This already imposes quite stringent relations
on the set $\{k\}$ as can be seen as follows. In order that we
get a satisfactory representation of the potential energy,
the set $\{k\}$ must necessarily contain a sufficient number of
k's which are larger than r_U^{-1}, if r_U is, say, the range of the
repulsive core of the potential energy. Put differently,
$d(x)$ must be a function with a narrow peak at the origin,
the width of the peak being less than r_U. As r_U will be of
the order of magnitude of a few angstroms, we must expect
the integers which multiply k_0 to range at least up to 10^8.
On the other hand, if we are dealing with a nearly perfect
gas, N will be of the order of 10^{18}, and we see that the
density of wave vectors $\mathbf{k}$ in the set $\{\mathbf{k}\}$ in the three-dimensional case will be extremely small, namely, of the order
of 10^{-6} per unit volume of $\mathbf{k}$-space. That the distribution
in k-space of the set $\{k\}$ must be random does not follow
immediately from the above considerations, but one must
enquire in more detail into the nature of the set $\{k\}$ which
will produce a delta-like $d(x)$. If $d(x)$ is, indeed, a function
with a peak narrower than r_U, we see that sums like that of
expression 6.310 will be small, as there will be very few configurations for which $x_j - x_n < r_U$, because of the repulsive
core of width r_U, and as long as $x_j - x_n > r_U$, $d(x_j - x_n)$ will
be practically equal to zero. As the expression of equation
6.310 can be written approximately as $(\dot{x}^2)_{Av} \sum_{j \neq n} d(x_j - x_n)$,
we see that, indeed, these terms will practically always be
negligibly small. Percus and Yevick (1956) give a more
detailed analysis of these terms and we refer to their paper
for more details.

The starting point of Percus and Yevick's second
method is similar to that of their first one, but proceeds
differently in finding the ν_k necessary to satisfy approximately
equation 6.305. They now minimize the time average of the
square of the difference between the left-hand side and the
right-hand side of equation 6.305, that is, they minimize
the integral I given by the equation

$I = \lim_{T\to\infty}$

$$\frac{1}{T}\int_0^T dt\,\{U(x_j - x_n) - \textstyle\sum_{\{k,\,0\}} \frac{\nu_k}{N^2 k^2}\exp[ik(x_j-x_n)]\}^2, \quad (6.311)$$

where we have included in the sum $\sum_{\{k,\,0\}}$ the term B, by putting

$$B = \lim_{k\to 0} (\nu_k/k^2).$$

The integration over time in equation 6.311 can be replaced by an integration over space, if we introduce the two-body distribution function $\sigma(x)$. This function is defined by the following equation, which should be valid for any function $g(x_j,\,x_n)$,

$$\lim_{T\to\infty} \frac{L^2}{T}\int_0^T g(x_j,x_n)\,dt = \iint g(x_j,x_n)\sigma(x_j-x_n)dx_j\,dx_n. \quad (6.312)$$

Using $\sigma(x)$ we can write equation 6.311 in the form

$$I = \frac{1}{L}\int \{U(x) - \textstyle\sum_{\{k,\,0\}} \frac{\nu_k}{N^2 k^2}e^{ikx}\}^2\,\sigma(x)dx, \quad (6.313)$$

and minimization of I leads to the following equations for the ν_k

$$\textstyle\sum_{\{k,\,0\}} \sigma_{k'-k}\,\nu_k/N^2 k^2 = (U\sigma)_{k'}. \quad (6.314)$$

Similarly one can express the f_k in terms of the Fourier components of $\sigma(x)$.

It is easily shown that equation 6.314 is approximately satisfied by equations 6.308. In order to see that we introduce a continuous variable u instead of the discrete variable k, and equation 6.314 can then be written in the form

$$\int \sigma(u' - u)u^{-2}\nu(u)\rho(u)du = N^2\int \sigma(u' - u)\,U(u)du, \quad (6.315)$$

where $\rho(u)$ is the density function of the set $\{k\}$. We see that

$$u^{-2} v(u) \rho(u) = N^2 U(u), \quad \text{or}, \quad v_k \rho_k = N^2 k^2 U(k), \quad (6.316)$$

is a solution of equation 6.315. From the fact that $d(x)$ approximates the delta-function, it follows that ρ_k is related to d_k by the equation

$$\rho_k d_k \doteq 1, \quad (6.317)$$

and we see that equation 6.316 leads approximately to equation 6.308.

In a later paper Percus and Yevick (1957d) consider in detail the statistics of a many-body system in terms of $\sigma(x)$. As the Hamiltonian is now an expression containing the σ_k in its coefficients and as, in turn, one can obtain $\sigma(x)$ from the Hamiltonian by the usual statistical methods, one obtains a self-consistent set of equations for $\sigma(x)$. This set of equations is solved in a virial expansion, and it is found that this theory can reproduce the first three virial coefficients exactly, and the fourth one to a fair approximation. We have not got the space to discuss these results or the discussion of quantum mechanical systems (Percus and Yevick 1957c, e) in detail.

In conclusion we want to show how $\sigma(x)$ is related to the average value of $|\xi_k|^2$. For this expression we have, using equation 6.312,

$$(|\xi_k|^2)_{\text{Av}} = (Nk)^{-2} \{N + \sum_{j \neq n} \exp [- ik(x_j - x_n)]\}_{\text{Av}}$$
$$= (Nk^2)^{-1} \{1 + (N - 1) (\exp [- ik(x_j - x_n)])_{\text{Av}}\}$$
$$= (Nk^2)^{-1} \{1 + (N - 1) L^{-1} \int \sigma(x) \exp (ikx) dx\}$$

or,

$$(|\xi_k|^2)_{\text{Av}} = (Nk^2)^{-1}[1 + (N - 1)\sigma_k]. \quad (6.318)$$

6.4 Redundant Variables, Subsidiary Conditions, and Auxiliary Fields

We have had several opportunities to mention the difficulties all theories of collective behaviour meet with in trying to find suitable particle coordinates as well as suitable collective coordinates. In Yevick and Percus' work this problem is not considered at all, as they work with just as many ξ_k as there are degrees of freedom. In Tomonaga's method the problem is by-passed only inasmuch as one fixes one's attention on the collective coordinates, leaving the determination of the particle coordinates as a future task — the only exception being Brenig's work on liquid helium (see Chapter 10). In the present and in the next section we shall describe some attempts to solve this problem. We unfortunately do not have the space to discuss these methods in detail, and we must refer the reader to the original literature for a detailed account of them. The methods discussed in the present section have all one feature in common, namely that they try to retain all $3N$ particle coordinates as well as the n collective coordinates. As the system is thus over-determined, it is necessary to impose constraints on the system. Although the methods discussed in the present section were developed using quantum mechanics, we shall give here the classical counterpart indicating, where necessary, modifications which must be made in the quantum mechanical case.

Zubarev (1953) in Russia and Bohm and Pines (1953, see also Pines 1955) in the United States have developed independently methods for introducing the ξ_k as extra collective coordinates. Bohm and Pines were only interested in the application of their method to the electron plasma case, while Zubarev kept his discussion more general. It can easily be shown that the two methods are equivalent, and we shall derive in fact Bohm and Pines' Hamiltonian from Zubarev's one. In the discussion, we hope, the differences in the starting points of the two methods will become clear. We may remark here that Galasiewicz (1956b) has shown the equivalence of the two methods in the quantum mechanical case. Our derivation of Zubarev's Hamiltonian is the classical counterpart of his method as modified by Migdal and Galitski (see Galasiewicz 1956a).

We start from the Hamiltonian

$$H = \sum_j (\mathbf{p}_j{}^2/2m) + \tfrac{1}{2} \sum_{j \neq n} U(r_{jn}). \qquad (6.401)$$

We now introduce a set of canonical variables $Q_\mathbf{k}$ and $P_\mathbf{k}$ corresponding to a set of n wave numbers $\{\mathbf{k}\}$. This set need not be specified any further, except that if $\mathbf{k}$ belongs to $\{\mathbf{k}\}$, $-\mathbf{k}$ must also belong to it. In most cases of interest the set $\{\mathbf{k}\}$ will be all those $\mathbf{k}$ for which $|\mathbf{k}|$ is less than a certain value k_0, say. As the $P_\mathbf{k}$ and $Q_\mathbf{k}$ do not appear in H, it follows from the canonical equations of motion that the possible orbits of the system in the $3N + n$-dimensional $\mathbf{x}_j$, $Q_\mathbf{k}$ space must all be constrained to lie on the hypersurfaces

$$Q_\mathbf{k} = \text{constant} = 0, \text{ say.} \qquad (6.402)$$

We may draw attention at this point to the similarity between the constraints of equation 6.402 and the constraints of equation 6.129 introduced by Skinner. There is, however, one important difference, namely, that while in Skinner's case the $\xi_\mathbf{k}$ are the collective coordinates *before* the transformation, here the $Q_\mathbf{k}$ are the collective coordinates only *after* the necessary transformation (see equation 6.405).

We now introduce a canonical transformation through a generating function $\Omega(P'_\mathbf{k}, Q_\mathbf{k}; \mathbf{p}'_j, \mathbf{x}_j)$ given by the equation

$$\Omega = \sum_{\{\mathbf{k}\}} P'_\mathbf{k}(Q_\mathbf{k} + \xi_\mathbf{k}) + \sum_j (\mathbf{p}'_j \cdot \mathbf{x}_j), \qquad (6.403)$$

where the $\xi_\mathbf{k}$ are functions of the $\mathbf{x}_j$ given by equation 6.204.

The equations connecting the $\mathbf{p}_j$, $\mathbf{x}_j$, $P_\mathbf{k}$, $Q_\mathbf{k}$ and the $\mathbf{p}'_j$, $\mathbf{x}'_j$, $P'_\mathbf{k}$, $Q'_\mathbf{k}$ are the usual ones (for instance, Goldstein 1950, Ch. 8),

$$Q'_\mathbf{k} = \frac{\partial \Omega}{\partial P'_\mathbf{k}}, \; \mathbf{x}'_j = \frac{\partial \Omega}{\partial \mathbf{p}'_j}; \; P_\mathbf{k} = \frac{\partial \Omega}{\partial Q_\mathbf{k}}, \; \mathbf{p}_j = \frac{\partial \Omega}{\partial \mathbf{x}_j}, \qquad (6.404)$$

which, if we use equations 6.402 and 6.204, take the form

$$Q'_\mathbf{k} = \xi_\mathbf{k}, \qquad (6.405)$$

$$P_\mathbf{k} = P'_\mathbf{k}, \qquad (6.406)$$

$$\mathbf{x}'_j = \mathbf{x}_j, \qquad (6.407)$$

$$\mathbf{p}_j = \mathbf{p}'_j - i \sum_{\{\mathbf{k}\}} (\mathbf{k}/Nk)P'_{\mathbf{k}} \exp\left[-i(\mathbf{k} \cdot \mathbf{x}_j)\right]. \quad (6.408)$$

Before introducing the new coordinates into the Hamiltonian, we write the potential energy in the form (compare equation 6.233)

$$\tfrac{1}{2}\sum_{j \neq n} U(r_{jn}) = U_0(\mathbf{x}_j) + \tfrac{1}{2}N^2 \sum_{\{\mathbf{k}\}} k^2 U(k)\, \xi_{\mathbf{k}}\, \xi_{-\mathbf{k}}, \quad (6.409)$$

$$U_0(\mathbf{x}_j) = \tfrac{1}{2}N^2 \sum_{\{\{\mathbf{k}\}\}} k^2 U(k)\, \xi_{\mathbf{k}}\, \xi_{-\mathbf{k}} - \tfrac{1}{2}N\sum_{\mathbf{k}} U(k), \quad (6.410)$$

where the first summation in equation 6.410 is over the set $\{\{\mathbf{k}\}\}$ which contains all $\mathbf{k}$ except those belonging to $\{\mathbf{k}\}$, and where the second summation is over all wave numbers $\mathbf{k}$.

We can now express the new Hamiltonian H' in the new coordinates, and the result is

$$H' = H_1(\mathbf{p}', \mathbf{x}') + H_2(\mathbf{p}', \mathbf{x}'; P', Q') + H_3(P', Q'), \quad (6.411)$$

where

$$H_1(\mathbf{p}', \mathbf{x}') = \sum (\mathbf{p}'^2_j/2m) + U_0(\mathbf{x}'_j), \quad (6.412)$$

$$H_2(\mathbf{p}', \mathbf{x}'; P', Q') = \frac{-i}{Nm} \sum_{j,\{\mathbf{k}\}} \frac{(\mathbf{k} \cdot \mathbf{p}'_j)}{k} \exp\left[-i(\mathbf{k} \cdot \mathbf{x}'_j)\right]$$
$$-\frac{1}{2N^2 m} \sum_{j,\{\mathbf{k}\},\{\mathbf{l}\}(\mathbf{k}+\mathbf{l}\neq 0)} P'_{\mathbf{k}} P'_{\mathbf{l}} \frac{(\mathbf{k} \cdot \mathbf{l})}{kl} \exp\left[-i(\mathbf{k} + \mathbf{l} \cdot \mathbf{x}'_j)\right], \quad (6.413)$$

$$H_3(P', Q') = \tfrac{1}{2}\sum_{\{\mathbf{k}\}} \left[N^2 k^2 U(k)\, Q'_{+\mathbf{k}}\, Q'_{-\mathbf{k}} + (Nm)^{-1} P'_{+\mathbf{k}}\, P'_{-\mathbf{k}}\right]. \quad (6.414)$$

The constraints of the system are now given by equation 6.405 which shows that in the transformed system the extra coordinates are the $\xi_{\mathbf{k}}$. Equations 6.411 to 6.414 give us, indeed, Zubarev's Hamiltonian with one modification. Because in quantum mechanics the two terms on the right-hand side of equation 6.408 do not commute, in the first term on the right-hand side of equation 6.413 $\mathbf{p}'_j$ must be replaced by $\mathbf{p}'_j - \tfrac{1}{2}\hbar k$ to obtain the quantum mechanical Hamiltonian operator.

We have now obtained the Hamiltonian in terms of the $3N + n$ coordinates $\mathbf{x}'_j$, $Q'_{\mathbf{k}}$ and their conjugate momenta, and at the same time expressed the constraints in those coordinates. The Hamiltonian of the collective modes is the sum of a number of Hamiltonians, $H_{\mathbf{k}}$, each referring to a particular wave vector $\mathbf{k}$,

$$H_{\mathbf{k}} = \tfrac{1}{2} N^2 k^2 U(k) Q_{+\mathbf{k}} Q_{-\mathbf{k}} + P_{+\mathbf{k}} P_{-\mathbf{k}}/2Nm. \quad (6.415)$$

We see that the $H_{\mathbf{k}}$ are the same as in the expression of equation 6.225 except for the extra term in the $\xi_{+\mathbf{k}} \xi_{-\mathbf{k}}$ in the expression of equation 6.225 arising from the kinetic energy and apart from a factor 2 which arises from the fact that each $H_{\mathbf{k}}$ occurs twice, once as $H_{+\mathbf{k}}$ and once as $H_{-\mathbf{k}}$.

We shall not discuss at this point any applications of Zubarev's method, but refer to Chapter 10 where it is applied to the case of liquid helium.

To obtain Bohm and Pines' Hamiltonian we use the following transformation ($-e$ = electronic charge)

$$Q'_{\pm\mathbf{k}} \to i(4\pi e^2 N^2)^{-\frac{1}{2}} a_{\pm\mathbf{k}}, \; P'_{\pm\mathbf{k}} \to i(4\pi e^2 N^2)^{\frac{1}{2}} b_{\pm\mathbf{k}}, \quad (6.416)$$

which reduces the expression of equation 6.411 to their Hamiltonian.

The constraint, or subsidiary condition, is now of the form

$$a_{\pm\mathbf{k}} = - i(4\pi e^2/k^2)^{\frac{1}{2}} \sum_j \exp\left[\mp i(\mathbf{k} \cdot \mathbf{x}_j)\right]. \quad (6.417)$$

To see the physical meaning of this constraint we consider the field $\mathbf{F}$ given by the expression

$$\mathbf{F}(\mathbf{x}) = (4\pi)^{\frac{1}{2}} \sum_{\mathbf{k}} a_{-\mathbf{k}} \frac{\mathbf{k}}{k} e^{i(\mathbf{k} \cdot \mathbf{x})}. \quad (6.418)$$

As the charge density in our system, ρ_{el}, is given by the equation (we assume that the system is enclosed in a unit volume),

$$\rho_{\mathrm{el}} = -e \sum_j \delta(\mathbf{x} - \mathbf{x}_j) = - e \sum_{j,\,\mathbf{k}} e^{i(\mathbf{k} \cdot \mathbf{x})} e^{-i(\mathbf{k} \cdot \mathbf{x}_j)}, \quad (6.419)$$

we see that equation 6.417 is a consequence of the equation

$$(\nabla \cdot \mathbf{F}) = 4\pi\rho_{\mathrm{el}}, \quad (6.420)$$

which shows that $\mathbf{F}$ can be considered to be the electric field strength. Indeed, that was the way in which Bohm and Pines arrived at their Hamiltonian. They started essentially from the Hamiltonian

$$H_{\mathrm{BP}} = \sum_j \frac{[\mathbf{p}_j - (e/c)\mathbf{A}(\mathbf{x}_j)]^2}{2m} + \int \frac{[\mathbf{F}(\mathbf{x})]^2}{8\pi} d^3\mathbf{x}, \quad (6.421)$$

where $\mathbf{A}(\mathbf{x})$ is the longitudinal vector potential. They then introduced the $a_\mathbf{k}$ and $b_\mathbf{k}$ through the equations

$$\mathbf{A}(\mathbf{x}) = (4\pi c^2)^{\frac{1}{2}} \sum_\mathbf{k} b_\mathbf{k} \frac{\mathbf{k}}{k} e^{i(\mathbf{k}\cdot\mathbf{x})}, \quad (6.422)$$

$$\mathbf{F}(\mathbf{x}) = -(4\pi)^{\frac{1}{2}} \sum_\mathbf{k} \dot{b}_\mathbf{k} \frac{\mathbf{k}}{k} e^{i(\mathbf{k}\cdot\mathbf{x})}, \quad (6.423)$$

and this last equation reduces to equation 6.418 because of the usual relations between the $a_\mathbf{k}$ and $b_\mathbf{k}$ of an electromagnetic field (for instance, Kramers 1957, § 86). Substituting the expressions of equations 6.422 and 6.418 into equation 6.421 leads to the expression of equation 6.411. In order that the electric field is really produced by the charges, equation 6.420 must hold which leads to the subsidiary condition of equation 6.417.

We shall return to Bohm and Pines' theory in Chapter 8, but here we wish first of all to refer to discussions by Tomonaga (1955a, b), Nishiyama (1954) and Kinoshita and Nambu (1954) for other aspects of the introduction of auxiliary field. Secondly we wish to refer to papers by Adams (1955), Kuper (1956), Nishiyama (1956), Watanabe (1956), and Bohm, Huang, and Pines (1957) for a discussion of the role and influence of subsidiary conditions. Finally we wish to sketch very briefly an alternate method to derive Bohm and Pines' Hamiltonian (see Pines 1955). This method starts from the Hamiltonian given by equation 6.401 and adds to it the terms

$$H_{\mathrm{add}} = \tfrac{1}{2} \sum_{\{\mathbf{k}\}} a'_{+\mathbf{k}} a'_{-\mathbf{k}} + i(4\pi)^{\frac{1}{2}} eN \sum_{\{\mathbf{k}\}} a'_{+\mathbf{k}} \xi'_{+\mathbf{k}}, \quad (6.424)$$

where the a'_k are related to the Q_k in the same way as the a_k are related to the Q'_k. Because of equation 6.402 this additional term is always zero for all permissible orbits. We can now use the same canonical transformation to obtain H', or we can use the extended Hamiltonian, $H + H_{add}$, to obtain the orbits of the system. However, the extended Hamiltonian is only equivalent to H provided we explicitly introduce the subsidiary conditions. The advantage of using H_{add} lies in the fact that according to Bohm and Pines for many problems, especially the determination of the ground state of the system, one can perform the necessary canonical transformations without explicitly introducing the subsidiary conditions.

6.5 Collective Motion in Quantum Mechanics

Although Zubarev's and Bohm and Pines' method were developed in quantum mechanical terms, we have seen that it is easily possible to state these theories in classical terms. This seems, however, not to be the case for the methods developed by Skyrme (1957) and by Hubbard (1957a, b). Unfortunately we do not have the space to discuss Hubbard's method in detail. It is based on a slight variation of Goldstone's work (1957) on the Brueckner model of the nucleus and employs infinite perturbation series obtained by switching the interparticle interaction on adiabatically. The perturbation series are simplified by dropping "self-energy" terms and replacing the interaction energy by a suitably modified interaction. We shall briefly return to Hubbard's work in Chapter 8. It seems to us that it might be possible to write also Hubbard's method in classical terms, though it would be extremely complicated.

To see how Skyrme's method works, we first of all consider the idealized case where the Hamiltonian can be split exactly into two parts,

$$H(\mathbf{x}_j) = H_1(\bar{x}) + H_2(Q), \qquad (6.501)$$

where $\bar{x}$ indicates a set of $3N - n$ internal coordinates and

Q a set of n collective coordinates. The eigenfunctions $\psi_{im}(\mathbf{x}_j)$ of the system can now be written as a product,

$$\psi_{im}(\mathbf{x}_j) = \chi_i(\bar{x})\,\varphi_m(Q) \qquad (6.502)$$

where ψ_{im}, χ_i, and φ_m satisfy the equations

$$H\psi_{im} = E_{im}\,\psi_{im}, \quad H_1\,\chi_i = E_i\,\chi_i,$$
$$H_2\,\varphi_m = E_m\,\varphi_m, \quad E_{im} = E_i + E_m. \qquad (6.503)$$

We may remark here that product wave functions such as given by equation 6.502 also play an important role in Bohm and Pines' discussion of electron interaction in metals (see, for instance, Pines 1955).

If we consider all eigenstates of H which correspond to one particular eigenstate of H_1, we see that the energy eigenvalues corresponding to these eigenstates will form an energy "band".

Let us now consider a more realistic state of affairs, where the exact separation of equation 6.501 is no longer possible, but where equation 6.501 is still a fair approximation. In that case we would expect that the complete eigenvalue spectrum will still show "bands" corresponding to eigenstates of the system with approximately the same internal motion. We can express this by writing for such a band

$$E = \varepsilon + E_m, \quad H\psi_m = E\psi_m = (\varepsilon + E_m)\psi_m. \quad (6.504)$$

If it still makes sense to talk about collective and internal motion, it must be possible to consider the E_m to be approximately equal to the eigenvalues e_m of a *model* Hamiltonian h which will be a function of a set of n coordinates ζ,

$$h\phi_m(\zeta) = e_m\,\phi_m(\zeta), \qquad (6.505)$$

$$e_m \doteq E_m. \qquad (6.506)$$

Skyrme now considers the extended system described by the $3N$ $\mathbf{x}_j$ and the n ζ. In his case the system is not over-determined, because he considers all states belonging to a complete band at the same time. To see this perhaps more clearly we remember that matrix mechanics is obtained from wave mechanics by a transformation from continuous variables, which are the coordinates, to the discrete variables, which are the quantum numbers. For instance, in equation 6.503 we have the first step of such transformations, namely, from the $\mathbf{x}$ to the i, and from the Q to m. Skyrme, in fact, introduces the inverse transformation from the quantum number m characterizing the energy levels in the band to the n ζ.

The next problem is how to find the Schrödinger equation for the extended system. Consider the function $F(\mathbf{x}, \zeta)$ given by the equation

$$F(\mathbf{x}, \zeta) = \sum_m \psi_m(\mathbf{x}) \phi_m^*(\zeta), \qquad (6.507)$$

where the $\psi_m(\mathbf{x})$ are the eigenfunctions corrseponding to the band (see equation 6.504). As we are considering a complete band, we can use for the $\phi_m(\zeta)$ a complete orthonormal set, and it follows from equation 6.507 that

$$\psi_m(\mathbf{x}) = \int F(\mathbf{x}, \zeta) \phi_m(\zeta) d^n\zeta. \qquad (6.508)$$

If the system were strictly separable, equation 6.505 would be the same as the third of equations 6.503 and we could write (see, for instance, Kramers 1957, p. 130)

$$\psi_m(\mathbf{x}) = \chi(\bar{x}) \varphi_m(Q), \quad \phi_m \equiv \varphi_m,$$
$$F(\mathbf{x}, \zeta) = \chi(\bar{x}) \sum_m \varphi_m(Q) \varphi_m^*(\zeta) = \chi(\bar{x}) \delta^{(n)}(Q - \zeta), \qquad (6.509)$$

where $\delta^{(n)}$ is the n-dimensional delta-function. We can use equation 6.509 as a guide to the form of $F(\mathbf{x}, \zeta)$ for the case when the system is only approximately separable.

If equation 6.506 were exactly satisfied instead of only approximately, it would follow from equations 6.504 to 6.507 that $F(\mathbf{x}, \zeta)$ would satisfy the equation

$$(H - h - \varepsilon)F(\mathbf{x}, \zeta) = 0. \qquad (6.510)$$

In general, equation 6.510 will not be satisfied exactly, but we can use a variational principle to determine ε and possible parameters in h and F by requiring that equation 6.510 is satisfied as well as possible, that is, by satisfying the variational equation

$$\delta \int F^*(\mathbf{x}, \zeta)[H - h - \varepsilon]^2 \, F(\mathbf{x}, \zeta) \, d^{3N}\mathbf{x} d^n \zeta = 0. \qquad (6.511)$$

Variation with respect to ε leads to the equation

$$\int F^*(H - h - \varepsilon) \, F \, d^{3N}\mathbf{x} d^n \zeta = 0. \qquad (6.512)$$

In many cases we know the form of h and often we can write

$$h = \sum_p \alpha_p h_p, \qquad (6.513)$$

where the h_p are given operators and where the α_p are parameters to be determined. Variation with respect to the α_p leads to the equations

$$\int F^* h_p (H - h - \varepsilon) F d^{3N}\mathbf{x} d^n \zeta = 0. \qquad (6.514)$$

In applications Skyrme has actually used instead of equation 6.511 the similar equation

$$\delta \int F^*(H - h - \varepsilon) F d^{3N}\mathbf{x} d^n \zeta = 0 \qquad (6.515)$$

for determining $F(\mathbf{x}, \zeta)$, and used equations 6.512 and 6.514 to get conditions for self-consistency.

We do not wish to discuss here any applications, but we refer to Skyrme's paper and to Chapters 8 and 9. We must remark at this point that, as was emphasized by Skyrme himself, this method is only applicable with any hope of success if we know the approximate nature of the collective behaviour. For instance, in the case of the electron plasma we know that the collective modes are approximately harmonic oscillator modes and in the case of the rotational states of nuclei that they correspond approximately to the eigenstates of a rotator.

CHAPTER 7

Sound Waves

In this chapter we shall discuss sound waves, that is, longitudinal waves, in both gases and solids. We shall apply Tomonaga's method as developed in Section 6.2, but we shall also briefly discuss some results obtained by Percus and Yevick's method which was decribed in Section 6.3.

The first section of this chapter deals with gases, both perfect gases and nearly perfect gases. We derive the velocity of sound for a perfect gas from Tomonaga's method. For a nearly perfect gas the correction to the velocity of sound obtained by Tomonaga's method agrees in the limit of long wave lengths and very weak interactions with the correction to the isothermal velocity of sound obtained from the usual formula. The same limiting result can also be obtained by Percus and Yevick's method. The isothermal sound velocity is obtained by a similarly crude method from Pines and Bohm's equations.

The discussion of sound waves in crystals is confined to a one-dimensional crystal with nearest neighbour interactions only. The correct dispersion relation is obtained by Tomonaga's method.

We do not discuss sound waves from a quantum mechanical point of view, but refer to the literature (Penrose 1954, Tomonaga 1950, 1955b, Nishiyama 1951, 1955).

7.1 Sound Waves in Gases

Let us briefly summarize the equations which are satisfied by the density ρ of a gas (for instance, Morse 1936). If ρ_0 and p_0 are the equilibrium values of ρ and p, ρ satisfies the wave equation.

$$\nabla^2 \rho - \frac{ap_0}{\rho_0} \frac{\partial^2 \rho}{\partial t^2} = 0, \tag{7.101}$$

where $a = 1$, if the waves travel in an isothermal medium, while a = ratio of the specific heats, γ, if the wave motion is adiabatic. If ρ_k is again the Fourier component of the density, given by equation 6.206, we find for ρ_k the equation

$$\ddot{\rho}_k + k^2(ap_0/\rho_0)\,\rho_k = 0, \tag{7.102}$$

showing that ρ_k behaves as a harmonic oscillator of frequency $k(ap_0/\rho_0)^{1/2}$. The velocity of sound, c, which is defined by the equation

$$c = \partial\omega_k/\partial k, \tag{7.103}$$

is given by the equation

$$c^2 = ap_0/\rho_0. \tag{7.104}$$

If we are dealing with a perfect gas, equation 7.104 can be written in the form

$$c^2 = ak_B T/m, \tag{7.105}$$

where k_B is Boltzmann's constant, T the absolute temperature, and m the mass of a particle.

If, on the other hand, we are dealing with a nearly perfect gas, we have instead of equation 7.104 the equation

$$c^2 = \partial p/\partial \rho, \tag{7.106}$$

which up to terms in ρ (second virial coefficient term) in the isothermal case leads to the formula,

$$c^2 = (k_B T/m)[1 + 2B\rho], \tag{7.107}$$

where (see, for instance, ter Haar 1954, p. 177)

$$B = (2\pi/m) \int_0^\infty [1 - \exp(-\beta U)]\, r^2\, dr, \tag{7.108}$$

where

$$\beta = 1/k_B T, \qquad (7.109)$$

and where $U(r)$ is the interatomic potential energy.

We shall use again the method of Section 6.2 and assume that we may use equation 6.225, which means *inter alia* that we assume the total potential energy to be given by the equation

$$U = \tfrac{1}{2} \sum_{j \neq n} U(\mathbf{x}_j - \mathbf{x}_n) = \tfrac{1}{2} \sum_{j \neq jn} U(r_{jn}). \quad (7.110)$$

The analysis is now quite simple, and we can immediately use equation 6.227 for the velocity of sound. The result is

$$c = \frac{\partial \omega}{\partial k} = \frac{\partial}{\partial k} \left[\frac{3}{Nm^2} \sum_j (\mathbf{k} \cdot \mathbf{p}_j)^2 + \frac{N}{m} k^2 U(k) \right]^{\tfrac{1}{2}} \quad (7.111)$$

Let us first of all consider the case of a perfect gas so that we can put $U(k) = 0$. Writing

$$\sum_j (\mathbf{k} \cdot \mathbf{p}_j)^2 \rightleftharpoons \tfrac{1}{3} Nk^2 \langle p^2 \rangle, \qquad (7.112)$$

where $\langle \ \rangle$ indicates here an average over all particles in the system, we find

$$c^2 = \langle p^2 \rangle / m^2 = \langle v^2 \rangle = 3k_B T/m. \qquad (7.113)$$

This is not the isothermal sound velocity, and we are not sure of the physical origin of the extra factor 3. According to van Kampen (1957) one should expect this factor in the case where all collisions (or interactions) are neglected. We refer to van Kampen's paper for a discussion of the dispersion relation under various circumstances (see also Section 8.2).

Let us now consider a nearly perfect gas and long wave lengths, that is, wave lengths which are long compared to the range of the intermolecular forces. In that case we have approximately,

$$U(k) = V^{-1} \int \exp\left[- i(\mathbf{k} \cdot \mathbf{x})\right] U(\mathbf{x}) d^3\mathbf{x}$$
$$\rightleftharpoons V^{-1} \int U(\mathbf{x}) d^3\mathbf{x} = (4\pi/V) \int_0^\infty U(r) r^2 dr, \qquad (7.114)$$

so that we get for the sound velocity the approximate equation (provided we drop the extra factor 3 in the first term)

$$c^2 \doteqdot (k_B T/m) + (4\pi N/mV) \int_0^\infty U(r) r^2 dr. \quad (7.115)$$

On the other hand we get from equations 7.107 and 7.108, assuming βU to be so small that we can write $\exp(-\beta U) \doteqdot 1 - \beta U$,

$$c^2 \doteqdot (k_B T/m) + (4\pi k_B T\rho/m^2) \int_0^\infty \beta U r^2 dr, \quad (7.116)$$

which leads to equation 7.115, if we use equation 7.109 and the relation $\rho = mN/V$. We see that in the limit of long wave lengths and weak intermolecular forces the Tomonaga method leads to the correct correction term for the isothermal sound velocity.

We may at this point mention two different methods for deriving equation 7.111. The first one is based on the equations of Pines and Bohm (1952) and the second on the related method of Percus and Yevick (1957b; compare Section 6.3).

Pines and Bohm start from equation 6.209 for S_k and calculate from that equation and the equation of motion in the form (compare equations 6.217 and 6.218)

$$m\ddot{\mathbf{x}}_j = -\boldsymbol{\nabla}_j U = -i \sum_{n(\neq j)} \sum_k \mathbf{k} U(k) \exp i(\mathbf{k} \cdot \mathbf{x}_{jn}) \quad (7.117)$$

the equations of motion for the S_k, using the random phase approximation. The argument runs as follows:

$$\dot{S}_k = \sum_j i(\mathbf{k} \cdot \mathbf{v}_j) \exp i(\mathbf{k} \cdot \mathbf{x}_j), \quad (7.118)$$

$$\ddot{S} = -\sum_j (\mathbf{k} \cdot \mathbf{v}_j)^2 \exp i(\mathbf{k} \cdot \mathbf{x}_j) + i \sum_j (\mathbf{k} \cdot \ddot{\mathbf{x}}_j) \exp i(\mathbf{k} \cdot \mathbf{x}_j). \quad (7.119)$$

The first term can be written approximately as

$$-\tfrac{1}{3}k^2 \langle v^2 \rangle \sum_j \exp i(\mathbf{k} \cdot \mathbf{x}_j) = -\tfrac{1}{3}k^2 \langle v^2 \rangle S_k, \quad (7.120)$$

and for the second term we get from equation 7.117

$$i \sum_j (\mathbf{k} \cdot \ddot{\mathbf{x}}_j) \exp i(\mathbf{k} \cdot \mathbf{x}_j) = \sum_{n \neq j} \sum_\mathbf{l} (\mathbf{k} \cdot \mathbf{l}) U(k)$$
$$\exp [i(\mathbf{k} + \mathbf{l} \cdot \mathbf{x}_j)] \exp [-i(\mathbf{l} \cdot \mathbf{x}_n)]. \quad (7.121)$$

Using the random phase approximation we see that the term over j will only lead to an appreciable contribution, provided $\mathbf{l} = -\mathbf{k}$, so that the triple sum reduces to the single sum

$$-k^2 U(k) \sum_n \exp i(\mathbf{k} \cdot \mathbf{x}_n) = -k^2 U(k) S_\mathbf{k}. \quad (7.122)$$

Equations 7.120 and 7.122 together lead to equation 7.111, but now without the embarrassing extra factor 3. It must be noted that the average $\langle v^2 \rangle$ enters in a slightly different manner into the two derivations.

Percus and Yevick's method is even more straightforward. They assume that the S_k will show harmonic behaviour and write therefore

$$\omega_k{}^2 = (\dot{S}_k \dot{S}_{-k})_{\mathrm{Av}} / (S_k S_{-k})_{\mathrm{Av}}. \quad (7.123)$$

From equation 7.118 we get for the numerator in the one-dimensional case

$$(\dot{S}_k \dot{S}_{-k})_{\mathrm{Av}} = Nk^2 \langle v^2 \rangle, \quad (7.124)$$

while for the denominator we can use equation 6.318 to write

$$(S_k \cdot S_{-k})_{\mathrm{Av}} = N[1 + (N - 1)\sigma_k], \quad (7.125)$$

where σ_k is again the Fourier component of the two-body distribution function. They now use the fact that in the limit of very long wave length we have (Green 1952, p. 75)

$$\lim_{k \to 0} \sigma_k = -L^{-1} \int [1 - \exp(-\beta U)] \, dx, \quad (7.126)$$

where L is the "volume" of the one-dimensional system. Combining equations 7.123, 7.124, 7.125, and 7.126, we see that again in the limit where only the second virial coefficient comes into play, the sound velocity obtained from equation 7.106 agrees with the sound velocity obtained by the method of collective coordinates.

We do not wish to discuss here sound waves in a
degenerate Fermi-Dirac gas — a case which can be discussed
very adequately using Tomonaga's method. We refer to the
literature (Tomonaga 1950, 1955b; Nishiyama 1951, 1955;
ter Haar 1957).

7.2   Sound Waves in Crystals

We shall confine ourselves to a one-dimensional chain
of identical atoms interacting with nearest neighbours only.
The analysis can be extended to the case of a simple cubic
lattice.

The Hamiltonian of the system is given by the equation
(Born and von Kármàn 1912, 1913)

$$H = \sum_j (p_j{}^2/2m) + \tfrac{1}{2}a \sum_j (x_{j+1} - x_j - d)^2, \quad (7.201)$$

where

$$d = L/N, \qquad (7.202)$$

with L the repeating distance of the usual periodic boundary
conditions of the crystal, which extends in the x direction,
and N the number of atoms in L. We have assumed here
that in equilibrium all atoms are equally spaced, a distance
d apart.

We shall assume that we may neglect the ξ-dependent
terms due to the internal kinetic energy. We shall again
use for the ξ_k the coordinates given by equation 6.204 so
that we can use equations 6.210, 6.211, and also

$$U^+ = U^- = U^{++} = U^{--} = 0 \qquad (7.203)$$

but for U^{+-} we must use the original equation

$$U^{+-} = \{\{U, \pi_{+k}\}, \pi_{-k}\}. \qquad (7.204)$$

Using equation 7.201 we can evaluate U^{+-}. In the one-
dimensional case we have for $\pi_{\pm k}$ instead of equations 6.202
the following equations

$$\pi_{\pm k} = \pm i \sum_j p_j \exp(\pm ikx_j), \qquad (7.205)$$

and we get

$$\{\{U, \pi_{+k}\}, \pi_{-k}\} = \sum_{j,\,n} (\partial^2 U/\partial x_j\,\partial x_n) \exp\left[ik(x_n - x_j)\right], \quad (7.206)$$

or

$$\{\{U, \pi_{+k}\}, \pi_{-k}\}$$
$$= -a\sum_j \{\exp[ik(x_{j+1} - x_j)] - 2 + \exp[ik(x_{j-1} - x_j)]\}. \quad (7.207)$$

We can now introduce the assumption that all $x_{j+1} - x_j - d$ are small. This means that we can, to a fair approximation, rewrite equation 7.207 in the following form

$$\{\{U, \pi_{+k}\}, \pi_{-k}\} \doteq -aN[e^{ikd} - 2 + e^{-ikd}]. \quad (7.208)$$

As $\{\{U, \pi_{+k}\}, \pi_{-k}\}$ is the coefficient of $\xi_{+k}\xi_{-k}$, we get for the frequency ω_k the equation (compare equations 6.225 and 6.227)

$$\omega_k{}^2 = (4a/m)\sin^2 \tfrac{1}{2}kd, \quad (7.209)$$

which is the usual dispersion relation (see, for instance, Peierls 1955, p. 14), which in the limit of small k leads to the Debye approximation (1912)

$$\omega_k = c\,|k|, \quad c^2 = ad^2/m. \quad (7.210)$$

CHAPTER 8

Plasma Oscillations

In 1929 Tonks and Langmuir (1929) discussed the occurrence of oscillations in gaseous discharge plasmas, but although Steenbeck (1932) and Kronig and Korringa (1943) applied the idea of the existence of an electron plasma in metals to specific problems it was not until Bohm and Pines (1952, 1953, Pines and Bohm 1952, Pines 1953, 1954, 1955, 1956) discussed in detail electron interactions that a more general interest was taken in the properties of electron plasmas in solids as opposed to those in gaseous discharges.

In the first section of the present chapter we shall derive the equation of motion for the plasma coordinates, discuss the so-called Debye length, and mention very briefly some of the applications of plasma theory to metallic properties such as the correlation energy of an electron gas, magnetic properties, and characteristic energy losses. We must refer for more details to a number of review articles which have recently appeared (Pines 1955, 1956, Raimes 1956, 1957).

In the second section we discuss in some more detail the dispersion relation for plasma waves and show how it can be derived by the methods of Tomonaga and Skyrme discussed in Chapter 6 or by kinetic theory methods.

8.1 Plasma Oscillations and the Theory of Metals

In the next section we shall apply some of the methods discussed in Chapter 6 to the special case of an electron gas, but we shall use here a different approach, namely the one given in the original paper of Pines and Bohm (1952) describing the classical theory of an electron gas. The potential energy U of a system of electrons is given by the equation

$$U = - \sum_{j \neq n} e^2 / r_{jn}, \tag{8.101}$$

where $-e$ is the electronic charge and r_{jn} the distance apart of the jth and nth electron. Assuming that our system is enclosed in a box of unit volume with periodic boundary conditions, we have the following Fourier expansion for U,

$$U = - \sum_{\mathbf{k}} (4\pi e^2 / k^2) \sum_{j \neq n} \exp[i(\mathbf{k} \cdot \mathbf{x}_j - \mathbf{x}_n)], \tag{8.102}$$

where the sum over $\mathbf{k}$ does not include a term with $\mathbf{k} = 0$ in order to take into account an assumed uniform background of positive charge needed to ensure the over-all neutrality of the system.

From Newton's equations of motion it follows that the acceleration $\ddot{\mathbf{x}}_j$ of the jth electron is governed by the equation (compare equation 7.117)

$$m\ddot{\mathbf{x}}_j = -\nabla_j U = \frac{-4\pi e^2 i}{m} \sum_{n, \mathbf{k}} \frac{\mathbf{k}}{k^2} \exp[i(\mathbf{k} \cdot \mathbf{x}_j - \mathbf{x}_n)]. \tag{8.103}$$

Using again equation 6.204 for $\xi_{\mathbf{k}}$ we find, using equation 8.103, the following equations of motion (compare equations 7.119 to 7.122)

$$\ddot{\xi} = - \tfrac{1}{3} k^2 \langle v^2 \rangle \xi_{\mathbf{k}} - \frac{4\pi e^2 N}{m} \xi_{\mathbf{k}} - \sum_{j, n, \mathbf{l}(\neq \mathbf{k})} \frac{4\pi e^2 (\mathbf{k} \cdot \mathbf{l})}{mkl^2 N}$$

$$\cdot \exp[-i(\mathbf{l} \cdot \mathbf{x}_n)] \exp[i(\mathbf{l} - \mathbf{k} \cdot \mathbf{x}_j)], \tag{8.104}$$

where the second term on the right-hand side is the term with $\mathbf{l} = \mathbf{k}$ taken from the last sum, where N is the total number of electrons (per unit volume) of the system, and where $\langle v^2 \rangle$ is an average value of the square of the speed of the electrons, the average being defined by the equality of the expression of equation 7.120 and the first term on the right-hand side of equation 7.119.

In the random phase approximation the sum in equation

8.104 is neglected. We shall drop it and refer to Appendix B for a justification of this procedure. The first term on the right-hand side of equation 8.104 would be present whether or not the electrons interacted, and we should expect thus that proper collective behaviour will occur only as long as that term is small compared to the next one, or, as long as

$$k^2 \langle v^2 \rangle \ll 4\pi e^2 N/m. \tag{8.105}$$

This inequality implies that collective behaviour will correspond to wave lengths $\lambda(= k^{-1})$ which are longer than the so-called Debye length (Debye and Hückel 1923) λ_D given by the equation

$$\lambda_D = k_B T/4\pi N e^2, \tag{8.106}$$

where we have put $\langle v^2 \rangle = 3k_B T/m$ (k_B: Boltzmann's constant, T: absolute temperature).

If the condition of equation 8.105 is satisfied, we get for the frequency of the collective modes the equation

$$\omega = (4\pi e^2 N/m)^{1/2} = \omega_p, \tag{8.107}$$

where ω_p denotes the so-called plasma frequency.

If we consider an electron gas with kinetic energy of about 3 ev a density of about 10^{12} cm^{-3}, λ_D is about 10^{-3} cm and ω_p about 5×10^{10} sec^{-1}. In the case of the gas of the conduction electrons in a metal we can no longer use classical statistics. However, equation 8.107 still holds and for $N \rightleftharpoons 10^{23}$ cm^{-1} we get $\omega_p \rightleftharpoons 2 \times 10^{16}$ sec^{-1} corresponding to an energy $\hbar\omega_p \rightleftharpoons 10$ ev.

That, indeed, λ_D should be the limiting wave length for collective behaviour can also be seen from the following argument. Consider a sphere of radius R in the system. The total potential energy of such a sphere will be of the order $N_R{}^2 e^2/R$, where $N_R(= 4\pi N R^3/3)$ is the total number of particles in the sphere. The exact value of the potential energy will, of course, depend on the distribution of the particles over the sphere. On the other hand, the total kinetic energy will be of the order $\frac{1}{2} N_R m \langle v^2 \rangle$. Collective behaviour will occur, if the total potential energy of the sphere is at least equal to the (disruptive) total kinetic energy, or, if

$$(4\pi N R^3/3)^2 e^2/R \gg 2\pi N R^3 m \langle v^2 \rangle/3, \qquad (8.108)$$

which leads to the inequality of equation 8.105.

A slightly different argument leading to the same result is one due to Langmuir. Let v be the average particle speed and w the speed of the collective waves. As long as $v \ll w$ the force on the particle will be, as if it were at rest. If, however, $v \gg w$ the average force on the particle due to the collective wave will tend to cancel out, as the particle covers many wave lengths during one period of oscillation. The organized collective motion will thus stop as soon as w becomes smaller than the average speed of the particles in the system. As $w = \omega_p/k$, the condition $w^2 > \langle v^2 \rangle$ for the occurrence of collective behaviour reduces to the inequality of equation 8.105.

We have seen how the Debye length enters to give us a cut-off for the wave numbers of the collective modes. Another point where λ_D enters is in the description of the short range interaction which is left over, once the collective modes are described by the $\xi_{\mathbf{k}}$. We mentioned in Chapter 6 that the residual particle interaction U_0 is essentially the original interaction minus those Fourier components the wave vectors of which correspond to the collective modes. If we introduce a sharp cut-off at $k_0 (= \lambda_D^{-1})$ we find for U_0

$$U_0 = \tfrac{1}{2} \sum_{j \neq n} U_0(r_{jn}), \quad U_0(r) = -\sum_{k > k_0} \frac{4\pi e^2}{k^2} e^{i(\mathbf{k}\mathbf{x})} = -\frac{e^2}{r} f(r),$$

$$f(r) = \frac{2}{\pi} \int_{k_0 r}^{\infty} \frac{\sin x}{x} \, dx \doteqdot e^{-k_0 r}. \qquad (8.109)$$

We see that U_0 corresponds to a screened Coulomb potential with screening length λ_D.

We, unfortunately, have not the space to discuss how

the plasma oscillation theory can be used to discuss metallic
properties. For such applications it is necessary to use the
quantum mechanical theory. Its main success has been
in a discussion of the correlation energy of an electron gas
(Pines 1955, Gell-Mann and Brueckner 1957, Sawada 1957,
Hubbard 1957b), but the influence of Coulomb interactions
on the electronic free energy (Zubarev 1954) and specific
heat (Pines 1955, Gell-Mann 1957), on magnetic properties
(Pines 1955, Kanazawa 1956a, 1957), on transport properties
(Gabor 1952, Pines 1955, Bardeen and Pines 1955, Blatt
1955, Ahiezer 1956, Barrie 1956, ter Haar 1957a), and on
spin-orbit interactions (Kanazawa 1956b) has also been
studied. A problem of special interest is whether or not
characteristic energy losses of electrons of about 10 ev can
be ascribed to the excitation of plasma modes. It seems
as if some cases can be thus ascribed, but that other cases
must involve other mechanisms. We refer to the extensive
literature on this subject (Kronig and Korringa 1943,
Kramers 1947, Ruthemann 1941, 1942, 1948, Lang 1948,
Lindhard 1954, Hubbard 1955a, Marton, Leder, and Mendlowitz 1955, Pines 1955, 1956, Fano 1956, Jull 1956, Ferrell
1956, 1957, Ferrell and Quinn 1957, Raimes 1957). In conclusion we must mention work done on plasma oscillations
in semi-conductors (Lampert 1956, Groschwitz and Siebertz
1956, Fröhlich and Doniach 1956, Dresselhaus, Kip, and
Kittel 1955) and on the influence of the periodic lattice
on plasma oscillations (Wolff 1953, Hubbard 1954, 1955b,
Kanazawa 1955, Pines 1955, Raimes 1957).

8.2   The Dispersion Relation for Plasma Waves

In many ways the dispersion relation for plasma waves
gives one of the nicest applications of some of the theories
discussed in Chapter 6, and we want to discuss them in some
detail. Tomonaga's theory leads to them very easily in the
form of equation 6.227 which now gives us the equation

$$\omega^2 = \omega_{\mathrm{p}}{}^2 + k^2 \langle v^2 \rangle, \qquad (8.201)$$

if we use the equation $U(k) = 4\pi e^2/k^2$ and the definition of ω_p given in equation 8.107.

Skyrme (1957) has shown how his method also leads to equation 8.201 in the suitable limit. To illustrate his method we shall, however, be less ambitious and only derive equation 8.107 here. We start from the Hamiltonian

$$H = \sum \frac{p_j^2}{2m} + \sum_{\mathbf{k}} \frac{2\pi e^2}{k^2} \sum_{j \neq n} \exp\left[i(\mathbf{k} \cdot \mathbf{x}_j - \mathbf{x}_n)\right], \qquad (8.202)$$

and introduce the model Hamiltonian h in the form

$$h = \tfrac{1}{2} \sum_{\mathbf{k}} \hbar\omega_{\mathbf{k}} \left[\zeta_{\mathbf{k}}^2 - \hbar^2 \frac{\partial^2}{\partial \zeta_{\mathbf{k}}^2} \right], \qquad (8.203)$$

corresponding to a sum of harmonic oscillator Hamiltonians. The $\omega_{\mathbf{k}}$ correspond to the α_p in equation 6.513. To simplify matters further we shall consider only one $\mathbf{k}$. For the trial wave function $F(\mathbf{x}, \zeta)$ we write

$$F(\mathbf{x}, \zeta) = \left[\prod_j \exp\,(i/\hbar)(\mathbf{p}_j \cdot \mathbf{x}_j) \right]$$
$$\exp\left[-\tfrac{1}{2}\alpha\xi_{\mathbf{k}}^2 - \tfrac{1}{2}\beta\zeta_{\mathbf{k}}^2 + \lambda\xi_{\mathbf{k}}\zeta_{\mathbf{k}} \right], \qquad (8.204)$$

which looks like a fair approximation to the expression of equation 6.509. We can now determine α, β, and λ from the variational principle and $\omega_{\mathbf{k}}$ from the consistency condition of equation 6.512. If we assume that the $\mathbf{p}_i$ are sufficiently small so that the product $\prod_j$ in equation 8.204 can be put equal to unity, and if we neglect higher-order terms in $\hbar$ (classical limit), we find

$$\alpha = \delta, \ \ \beta = \delta^{1/2}, \ \ \gamma = \delta^{3/4}, \ \ \delta = 4m^2\,\omega_p{}^2/\hbar^2\,k^4, \ \ \omega = \omega_p. \ \ (8.205)$$

We see that in the limit $\hbar \to 0$, $F(\mathbf{x}, \zeta)$ reduces exactly to the expression of equation 6.509.

In conclusion we wish to mention van Kampen's work (1955, 1957) on the dispersion relation. He derives this relation starting from the transport equation (see also Vlasov 1945) in the form

$$\frac{\partial f_1}{\partial t} + (\mathbf{v} \cdot \boldsymbol{\nabla}) f_1 - \frac{eN}{m} (\mathbf{E} \cdot \boldsymbol{\nabla}_\mathbf{v}) f_0 = 0, \qquad (8.206)$$

where $\mathbf{E}$ is the averaged electric field strength

$$\mathbf{E}(\mathbf{x}, t) = - e \int \frac{(\mathbf{x} - \mathbf{x}') \, d^3 \mathbf{x}'}{|\mathbf{x} - \mathbf{x}'|^3} \int f_1(\mathbf{x}', \mathbf{v}', t) \, d^3 \mathbf{v}', \qquad (8.207)$$

$f(\mathbf{x}, \mathbf{v}, t)$ the distribution function,

$$f(\mathbf{x}, \mathbf{v}, t) = N f_0(v) + f_1(\mathbf{x}, \mathbf{v}, t), \qquad (8.208)$$

and $\boldsymbol{\nabla}_\mathbf{v}$ the velocity gradient differential operator. Equation 8.206 is derived from the usual transport equation (for instance, ter Haar 1954, equation 2.505) by neglecting all collisions, all fluctuations in $\mathbf{E}$, and higher-order terms in f_1.

We now ask for solutions of the form

$$f_1(\mathbf{x}, \mathbf{v}, t) = g(\mathbf{v}) \, e^{i(\mathbf{k} \cdot \mathbf{x}) - i\omega t}. \qquad (8.209)$$

Substitution of the expressions of equations 8.207 and 8.209 into equation 8.206 leads to the equation

$$[\omega - (\mathbf{k} \cdot \mathbf{v})] g(\mathbf{v}) = - (\omega_\mathbf{p}^2 / k^2)(\mathbf{k} \cdot \boldsymbol{\nabla}_\mathbf{v}) f_0 \int g(\mathbf{v}') d^3 \mathbf{v}', \quad (8.210)$$

and we see by integrating over $\mathbf{v}$, that solutions of the kind considered can only occur provided

$$\frac{\omega_\mathbf{p}^2}{k^2} \int \frac{(\mathbf{k} \cdot \boldsymbol{\nabla}_\mathbf{v}) f_0 \, d^3 \mathbf{v}}{(\mathbf{k} \cdot \mathbf{v}) - \omega} = 1. \qquad (8.211)$$

If $(\mathbf{k} \cdot \mathbf{v}) < \omega_\mathbf{p}$ we can evaluate the integral as a power series in $(\mathbf{k} \cdot \mathbf{v})/\omega_\mathbf{p}$. The first two terms lead to equation 8.201. It may be objected that, in general, $(\mathbf{k} \cdot \mathbf{v})$ cannot be smaller than $\omega_\mathbf{p}$ for *all* values of $\mathbf{v}$. This poses a problem which has been discussed in detail by van Kampen (1955; see also Landau 1946, Bohm and Gross 1949, Twiss 1952, Ecker 1955a, b, c, d, Berz 1956, Clemmow and Willson 1956, van Kampen 1957 — in this last paper van Kampen also discusses the case where collisions are so frequent that local equilibrium is established). We cannot enter into a detailed discussion, but may point out the solution of this problem. Strictly speaking there does not exist a dispersion relation, that is, there are no stationary solutions of the form of equation 8.209. However, even though all solutions of this form will be damped, there are solutions which have a very long lifetime, namely those for which equation 8.211 holds.

CHAPTER 9

Collective Behaviour of Nuclei

In Section 4.1 we discussed briefly the fact that nuclei show both collective and particle behaviour. In the present chapter the collective behaviour will be discussed. In the first section we give a brief survey of some of the collective aspects of nuclear behaviour, and in the last section we show how theories of collective behaviour can describe such phenomena as the giant resonance photo effect, surface oscillations, and rotational states.

9.1 General Discussion

When it became clear that nuclei show particle behaviour (shell model) as well as collective behaviour, Hill and Wheeler (1953) and Bohr and Mottelson (1953, see also Bohr 1952) developed a so-called *unified* model including both aspects. In Chapter 4 we were especially interested in justifying the existence of shell model characteristics, and now we are mainly interested in collective aspects, but it is perhaps of some interest to discuss just one aspect of the interaction of those two modes, namely the nuclear quadrupole moments. In the shell model one usually assumes a spherically symmetric closed-shell core. If this core really existed, the quadrupole moments should be due only to the extra nucleons. This leads, however, to moments which are an order of magnitude smaller than the experimentally observed ones, and the only possible explanation seems to be (Rainwater 1950, van Wageningen and de Boer 1952) that the extra nucleons will deform the core; this leads, indeed, to moments of the right order of magnitude.

The first collective mode of interest in nuclear theory is the centre-of-mass motion. As the total number of particles in a nucleus is not extremely large, the fact that this motion takes up three of the available degrees of freedom is not without importance. As we discussed in Chapter 6 this collective mode is usually very easily taken care of. It was briefly discussed by Skyrme (1957), and Tamura (1956) and Lipkin, de Shalit, and Talmi (1955) have discussed it using the method of redundant variables, Tamura essentially in the quantum mechanical analogue of the method of Section 6.4, Lipkin, de Shalit, and Talmi by a slightly more involved method.

A collective mode, which is nearly as simple, is the one where the protons and the neutrons vibrate out of phase, which may be a very simplified model leading to the so-called giant resonance effect (Goldhaber and Teller 1948). This model can be treated by Tomonaga's method as has been shown by Fujita (1956) or by the method of redundant variables (Ferentz, Gell-Mann, and Pines 1953). More complicated collective modes are those corresponding to the surface oscillations of the nucleus. They have especially been discussed by Bohr and Mottelson (1953), and Miyazima and Tamura (1956), and Zubarev (1955) have shown how they can be treated by the methods discussed in Chapter 6. Bohr (1952) postulated the following Hamiltonian for the surface oscillations. Let the surface of the nucleus in polar coordinates be described by the equation

$$R(\theta, \varphi) = R_0[1 + \sum_{l, m} \alpha_{lm} P_l^m(\theta, \varphi)], \qquad (9.101)$$

where R_0 is the equilibrium radius of the spherical nucleus, and where P_l^m are spherical harmonics. The α_{lm} are the collective coordinates describing the surface oscillations. It is now assumed that the collective Hamiltonian will be of the form

$$H(\alpha_{lm}) = \tfrac{1}{2}\sum_{l, m}[A_l|\pi_{lm}|^2 + B_l|\alpha_{lm}|^2], \qquad (9.102)$$

where the A_l and B_l are phenomenological coefficients which can be related to the nuclear density, radius, charge, and surface tension, and where the π_{lm} are the momenta canonically conjugate to the α_{lm}.

The last nuclear collective modes we wish to discuss are the rotational ones. Experimentally one knows that there are several nuclei which show rotational bands, that is, energy levels which are of the form

$$E = CI(I + 1), \ I \text{ integer.} \tag{9.103}$$

These rotational states can be treated either by the method of redundant variables (Lipkin, de Shalit, and Talmi 1955) or by Skyrme's method. We refer to a paper by Bohr (1954) for an extensive discussion of these rotational states and of the physical meaning of the quantum number I. The constant C in equation 9.103 is related to the moment of inertia of the nucleus.

In the restricted space at our disposal we unfortunately cannot discuss the various attempts to justify the nuclear Hamiltonian which differ from the methods discussed in Chapter 6, and we must refer to the literature (for instance, Bohr and Mottelson 1953, Süssmann 1954, Tolhoek 1954, 1955, Coester 1955).

9.2   Application of the Methods of Chapter 6

We now want to show how the collective phenomena briefly mentioned in the preceding section can be fitted into the general framework of Chapter 6. Let us first of all discuss the centre-of-mass motion. We saw in Section 6.1 how Tomonaga's method can deal with it. Let us see here, how the method of redundant variables would cope. The three collective coordinates to be introduced are clearly the components of the vector $\boldsymbol{\xi}$ given by the equation

$$\boldsymbol{\xi} = N^{-1} \sum_j \mathbf{x}_j. \tag{9.201}$$

The transformation function Ω will now be of the form

$$\Omega = \sum_j (\mathbf{p}_j' \cdot \mathbf{x}_j - \boldsymbol{\xi}) + (\mathbf{P}' \cdot \mathbf{Q} + \boldsymbol{\xi}), \tag{9.202}$$

and the transformation equations are of the form

$$\mathbf{x}'_j = \mathbf{x}_j - \boldsymbol{\xi}, \quad \mathbf{Q}' = \boldsymbol{\xi}, \quad \mathbf{P} = \mathbf{P}', \quad \mathbf{p}_j = \mathbf{p}'_j + (\mathbf{P}' - \sum \mathbf{p}'_n)/N, \tag{9.203}$$

where we have used the subsidiary condition $\mathbf{Q} = 0$. The kinetic energy expressed in the new variables is now of the well-known form

$$T' = \sum_j \frac{\mathbf{p}'^2_j}{2m} - \frac{(\sum \mathbf{p}'_j)^2}{2mN} + \frac{\mathbf{P}'^2}{2mN}, \tag{9.204}$$

which is also obtained by combining the equations $T = T_{\text{in}} + T_{\text{c}} = (T - T_{\text{c}}) + T_{\text{c}}$ and equations 6.126, 6.115, and 6.117.

The next case is that of the giant resonance phenomenon where we can use for Tomonaga's potential function ϕ the expression

$$\phi(\mathbf{x}) = t\mathbf{x}, \tag{9.205}$$

where

$$\left. \begin{array}{l} t_j = Z^{-1} \text{ if the } j\text{th particle is a proton,} \\ t_j = -N^{-1} \text{ if the } j\text{th particle is a neutron.} \end{array} \right\} \tag{9.206}$$

(One could express t more elegantly in terms of the isotopic spin.) The physical meaning of the corresponding collective coordinates $\boldsymbol{\xi}$ which according to equation 6.109 are given by

$$\boldsymbol{\xi} = B \sum_j t_j \mathbf{x}_j, \quad B = ZN/A, \tag{9.207}$$

where Z, N, and A are the total number of protons, neutrons, and nucleons, is that it is the vector from the centre of mass of the neutrons to the centre of mass of the protons. It may be noted that B is the ratio of the reduced mass involved in the dipole radiation and the nucleon mass.

The corresponding momentum $\boldsymbol{\pi}$ is given by equation 6.105, or

$$\boldsymbol{\pi} = \sum t_j \mathbf{p}_j, \tag{9.208}$$

and equation 6.106 is exactly valid. The vector $\boldsymbol{\pi}$ is essentially the momentum involved in the dipole vibration.

From the physical meaning of $\boldsymbol{\xi}$ it follows that the Hamiltonian describing the dipole interaction between nucleus and electromagnetic radiation will depend only on $\boldsymbol{\xi}$. Fujita (1956) has used $\boldsymbol{\xi}$ to describe the giant resonance photo effect, and we refer to his paper for a discussion of the Hamiltonian, the influence of exchange forces, and the relation to other collective models.

Let us now consider the case of the surface oscillations. We shall restrict ourselves to the case $\lambda = 2$. If $\lambda = 1$ we are led back to the centre-of-mass motion and the case $\lambda > 2$ is too complicated for our present discussion. We may remark that most discussions of surface oscillations are restricted to the case $\lambda = 2$.

We introduce the five potential functions

$$\phi_m(\mathbf{x}) = r^2 P_2{}^m, \quad m = 0, \pm 1, \pm 2, \qquad (9.209)$$

where we now for the sake of definiteness choose for the $P_l{}^m$ the normalization of Kramers (1957, p. 174). We assume that we may replace the sum in equation 6.109 by an integral so that we have the following collective coordinates

$$\xi_m = A_m{}^{-1}\int \phi_m d^3\mathbf{x}, \quad A_m = \int (\boldsymbol{\nabla}\phi_m{}^* \cdot \boldsymbol{\nabla}\phi_m) d^3\mathbf{x}. \quad (9.210)$$

It can be shown (ter Haar 1957) that for small values of α_{lm}, the ξ_m are essentially the α_{2m}. The conjugate momenta are given by the equations

$$\pi_m = (-1)^m \int (\mathbf{p} \cdot \boldsymbol{\nabla}\phi_m) d^3\mathbf{x}, \qquad (9.211)$$

and, provided the nucleus is nearly spherical and provided the total angular momentum $\mathbf{M}$, given by the equation

$$\mathbf{M} = \int [\mathbf{x} \wedge \mathbf{p}] d^3\mathbf{x}, \qquad (9.212)$$

vanishes, the π_m, ξ_m form a set of canonical variables (see ter Haar 1957) satisfying the relations

$$\{\xi_m, \pi_{m'}\} = \delta_{mm'}, \quad \{\xi_m, \xi_{m'}\} = \{\pi_m, \pi_{m'}\} = 0. \quad (9.213)$$

We can now use Tomonaga's procedure to find the collective kinetic energy, and the result is

$$T_c = \sum_m D_m |\pi_m|^2, \qquad (9.214)$$

where the D_m are proportional to $\mu^{-1} R_0^{-5}$ (μ is the nucleon mass). The expression of equation 9.214 for T_c is similar to the one used by Bohr. We could also derive the term in $|\xi_m|^2$, but this would involve making assumptions about the internucleon potential. We refer to Miyazima and Tamura's paper for a discussion of the potential energy and of the consequences of the Hamiltonian derived in this manner.

To conclude this chapter we wish to indicate how Skyrme's method can be used to obtain the effective moment of inertia of the nucleus (Skyrme 1957a). In this particular case we know that the model Hamiltonian should be of the form

$$h = J^2/2I, \qquad (9.215)$$

where J^2 is the operator corresponding to the square of the total angular momentum. The variational problem is now of the form

$$\delta \int F^*[H - h - \varepsilon]^2 F \, d\tau = 0. \qquad (9.216)$$

Variation of F leads to

$$(H - h)F = \varepsilon F, \qquad (9.217)$$

and variation of I and ε, and elimination of ε to

$$\frac{1}{2I} = \frac{\langle HJ^2 \rangle - \langle H \rangle \langle J^2 \rangle}{\langle J^4 \rangle - \langle J^2 \rangle^2}, \qquad (9.218)$$

where the $\langle \ \rangle$ indicate averages with respect to the F determined (or approximately determined) from equation 9.217. We refer to Skyrme's paper (1957a) for a discussion of the variational problem and only mention here that he finds for I approximately one half of the rigid moment. This seems to be in reasonable agreement with experimental data. It needs hardly be mentioned that in working out the expression of equation 9.218 it is necessary to make several simplifying assumptions. As was mentioned in Section 6.5, Skyrme's method is only feasible provided one has some idea about the form of the extended wave function F which, in the present case, is a function of the nucleon coordinates and of the Euler angles describing the orientation of the nucleus.

CHAPTER 10

Liquid Helium

Superconductivity and the behaviour of liquid helium below its λ-point are two low temperature phenomena which have exercised theorists off and on for the last few decades. Although the λ-transition of helium itself may not yet have been satisfactorily explained, at the present time it looks as if it is possible to explain the behaviour of liquid helium near the absolute zero starting from first principles. In the first section of the present chapter we shall very briefly discuss some of the recent work on this aspect of liquid helium. For more extensive discussions we refer to review articles by Chalatnikow (1956a, b) and Wilks (1957). In the last section we briefly discuss the application of Zubarev's method to liquid helium and Brenig's work.

10.1 Introduction

The forces between helium atoms can be derived more or less satisfactorily from first principles (Slater 1928, Rosen 1931, 1950, Margenau 1931a, b, 1939, Slater and Kirkwood 1931; for a general survey see Keesom 1942). It turns out that the forces are very weak so that it is tempting to treat liquid helium, at any rate to a first approximation, as being an ideal Bose-Einstein system, and the superficial similarity between the λ-transition and the so-called Einstein condensation (Einstein 1925, London 1938, Fowler and Jones 1938; for a general discussion see, for instance, ter Haar 1954) has lent some support to this point of view. Feynman (1953a, Chester 1954a, b) made it plausible that the weak interactions would not essentially alter this conclusion. However, Feynman's analysis starts from the gaseous state and the first phase transition encountered starting from high temperatures is indentified with the λ-transition. It seems thus that Feynman's theory does not take the ordinary gas-liquid transition properly into account, and as also his approximations seem doubtful (ter Haar 1954a) it seems that the last word on this topic still remains to be written.

Of more interest for our present discussion is the behaviour of liquid helium near the absolute zero. Landau (1941, 1947; see also Kronig and Thellung 1952, Thellung 1953, 1956, Ziman 1953, Allcock and Kuper 1955) derived from a quantization of the hydrodynamical equations the following expression for the energy $E(k)$ as a function of the wave number k,

$$E(k)=\hbar ck, \ k\ll k_0; \ E(k)=\varDelta+\hbar^2(k-k_0)^2/2\mu, \ k\sim k_0, \quad (10.101)$$

where c, $\varDelta$, k_0, and μ are parameters. This form of the energy spectrum is sufficient to explain both the observed second sound velocity and the observed specific heat data, and as $\partial E/\partial k \neq 0$ for $k = 0$ it leads to superfluidity. The lower part of the spectrum ($k \ll k_0$) corresponds to longitudinal waves, the so-called phonons, while the spectrum for $k \sim k_0$ is said to correspond to rotons. It may be remarked here that the use of the term rotons hardly seems fully justified as there appears to be a gradual transition from excitations of small wave number to those of larger wave number. There seems thus to be no other justification for the continued use of the term rotons for these excitations than that it enables us to describe the behaviour of liquid helium using the two-fluid model.

One would, of course, like to derive the energy spectrum of equation 10.101 from first principles. One way of doing this, to be discussed in the next section, would be to use collective longitudinal modes to describe the phonons and continue from there. Another mode of attack is the straight-forward quantum mechanical way used by Feynman (1953b,

1954, 1955, Feynman and Cohen 1956) which we shall discuss briefly in the present section. In Feynman's considerations the Bose statistics of the helium atoms play an important role. They are responsible for the fact that the only excitations of small energy will be those of long wave lengths. The wave function Ψ corresponding to such an excitation will essentially be the ground-state wave function Φ modulated by our $\xi_{\mathbf{k}}$ given by equation 6.204, or

$$\Psi = a\xi_{\mathbf{k}}\Phi = a' \left[\sum_j \exp i(\mathbf{k} \cdot \mathbf{x}_j)\right]\Phi(\mathbf{x}_j), \quad (10.102)$$

where the a and a' are normalizing constants. One can easily check that the Ψ lead, indeed, to the phonon spectrum. Feynman (1954) has shown that the expression of equation 10.102 is also a good approximation for the wave functions of the "rotons" which shows that the distinction between phonons and rotons is at best extremely tenuous.

Let us consider the energy corresponding to this wave function. For the ground state wave function we have $H_{\mathrm{op}}\Phi = 0$, if we use for the Hamiltonian H_{op} the expression

$$H_{\mathrm{op}} = -(\hbar^2/2m) \sum_j \mathbf{\nabla}_j^2 + U - E_0, \quad (10.103)$$

where E_0 is the ground state energy. For $H_{\mathrm{op}}\Psi$ we get

$$H_{\mathrm{op}}\Psi = -\frac{a\hbar^2}{2m\Phi} \sum_j (\mathbf{\nabla}_j \cdot |\Phi|^2 \mathbf{\nabla}_j \xi_{\mathbf{k}}), \quad (10.104)$$

and the energy of this state is given by the equation

$$E(k) = \frac{\hbar^2}{2m} \frac{\int |\Phi|^2 \sum_j (\mathbf{\nabla}_j \xi_{-\mathbf{k}} \cdot \mathbf{\nabla}_j \xi_{\mathbf{k}})d\tau}{\int |\Phi|^2 |\xi_{\mathbf{k}}|^2 d\tau}, \quad (10.105)$$

which reduces to the expression

$$E(k) = \hbar^2 k^2 / 2m\sigma_{\mathbf{k}}, \quad (10.106)$$

where $\sigma_{\mathbf{k}}$ is the Fourier coefficient of the two-body distribution function as in Section 6.3, and where we have used equations 6.204 and 6.318 and neglected terms of the relative order N^{-1}. The function $\sigma_{\mathbf{k}}$ can be obtained from neutron diffraction data (Reekie and Hutchison 1953, Goldstein and Reekie 1955) and leads to an $E(k)$ in good agreement with the spectrum necessary to explain the experimental data for the whole range of k.

Especially, the local structure produced by an approximate equal spacing of the atoms in the ground state will lead to a maximum of $\sigma_\mathbf{k}$ for $k \sim 2\pi/d$, where d is the average distance apart of the atoms. This maximum of $\sigma_\mathbf{k}$ will lead to the minimum of $E(k)$ near k_0.

10.2   The Collective Approach to Liquid Helium

We shall first of all consider briefly the application of Zubarev's method and then give a brief description of Brenig's work (1956). Bogoliubov and Zubarev (1955, Zubarev 1955) have used the method of auxiliary variables to obtain the wave function of the ground state of a Bose system with weak interactions. The first step is to express the Hamiltonian in terms of the $\xi_\mathbf{k}$. Using essentially the random phase approximation they are led to the following Schrödinger equation

$$i\hbar\,\frac{\partial \Phi'}{\partial t} = \tfrac{1}{2}\left\{\sum_\mathbf{k} E(k)\left[q_\mathbf{k}q_{-\mathbf{k}} - \frac{\partial^2}{\partial q_\mathbf{k}\,\partial q_{-\mathbf{k}}}\right]\right\}\Phi', \ (10.201)$$

where

$$\Phi' = \exp\left[-\,(4Nk^2)^{-1}\sum_\mathbf{k}\xi_\mathbf{k}\xi_{-\mathbf{k}}\right]\Phi, \qquad (10.202)$$

$$q_\mathbf{k} = (Nk^2/2\lambda_k{}^2)\,\xi_\mathbf{k}, \qquad\qquad (10.203)$$

$$[E(k)]^2 = (NU(k)\hbar^2 k^2/m) + (\hbar^2 k^2/2m)^2, \quad (10.204)$$

$$\lambda_k{}^4[NU(k) + (\hbar^2 k^2/4m)] = \hbar^2 k^2/4m, \qquad (10.205)$$

and where Φ is the wave function of the system. The $U(k)$ are again determined through equation 6.218, and the volume of the system is taken to be unity. The ground state wave function of equation 10.201 is $\exp\left[-\tfrac{1}{2}\sum_\mathbf{k} q_\mathbf{k} q_{-\mathbf{k}}\right]$, and the total wave function of the ground state is given by the equation

$$\Phi_0 = \exp\left[(4Nk^2)^{-1}\sum_{\mathbf{k}}(1 - \lambda_k^{-2})\xi_{\mathbf{k}}\xi_{-\mathbf{k}}\right]. \quad (10.206)$$

This wave function is similar to the one derived by Bijl (1940). It is interesting to note that if there is no interaction $\lambda_k = 1$, and the wave function reverts to a constant, the excited states correspond to wave functions of the shape given by equation 10.102 with Φ given by equation 10.206. The λ_k are directly related to σ_k; in fact, σ_k is proportional to $\lambda_k^2 - 1$.

Although Brenig's work does not lead to any quantitative results, it is of interest in that Brenig attempts with some success to introduce particle coordinates as well as collective coordinates. His method contains ideas from all the different methods discussed in Chapter 6, although it is mainly based on Tomonaga's work. It would be of interest to extend his work to obtain quantitative results from it for the behaviour of liquid helium at finite temperatures.

The collective coordinates used by Brenig are again essentially the $\xi_{\mathbf{k}}$ given by equation 6.204; with the conjugate momenta $\pi_{\mathbf{k}}$ given by equation 6.202, equations 6.231 for the Poisson brackets of the ξ and π are again satisfied in the random phase approximation. The set $\{\mathbf{k}\}$ corresponding to the collective coordinates will contain N wave numbers, corresponding to the longitudinal modes of our system of N particles which is enclosed in a volume taken to be unity. We take for these N wave numbers those satisfying the relation (compare equation 6.303 for the permissible values of $\mathbf{k}$),

$$|\mathbf{k}| \leqq k_0, \quad \frac{4\pi}{3}\left(\frac{k_0}{2\pi}\right)^3 = N. \quad (10.207)$$

We shall assume that there is no dispersion which corresponds to assuming that $U(k)$ is a constant for all $\mathbf{k}$ belonging to $\{\mathbf{k}\}$ (see equation 7.111), and neglecting the kinetic energy term in the coefficient of $\xi_{+\mathbf{k}}\xi_{-\mathbf{k}}$ we have for the collective Hamiltonian H_c (compare equation 6.415),

$$H_c = T_c + U_c, \quad T_c = \tfrac{1}{2}\sum_{\{\mathbf{k}\}} \pi_{+\mathbf{k}} \pi_{-\mathbf{k}}/Nm,$$
$$U_c = \tfrac{1}{2}\sum_{\{\mathbf{k}\}}^{*} Nmk^2 c^2 \xi_{+\mathbf{k}} \xi_{-\mathbf{k}}, \quad (10.208)$$

where c is the velocity of sound (compare equation 7.111).

For the particle coordinates we can use $2N/3$ of the $\mathbf{x}_j$. These $2N$ coordinates will be denoted by q. The $\mathbf{x}_j$ are not independent as they satisfy the N equations

$$\sum_j \exp\left[i(\mathbf{k}\cdot\mathbf{x}_j]\right] = Nk\xi_{\mathbf{k}}, \quad (10.209)$$

so that there are, indeed, $2N$ degrees of freedom left for the q.

From equation 10.208 it follows easily that for $k < k_0$, the energy is given by the expression $E(k) = \hbar ck$. The problem is how to find $E(k)$ for $k > k_0$. In order to do this we use the adiabatic, Born-Oppenheimer approximation, that is, we assume that we may write for the wave function Ψ,

$$\Psi = \varphi(q,\ \xi^{(0)})\psi(\xi), \quad (10.210)$$

where $\xi^{(0)}$ indicates a fixed set of values of the $\xi_{\mathbf{k}}$. As in the applications of Skyrme's method we shall use for $\psi(\xi)$ a function approximating a delta function, and in particular we shall use the function

$$\psi(\xi) = \prod_{\{\mathbf{k}\}}(\pi\alpha_k)^{-\frac{1}{4}} \exp\left(-\frac{\xi_{+\mathbf{k}}\xi_{-\mathbf{k}}}{2\alpha_k}\right), \quad \alpha_k = \frac{\lambda}{kN}, \quad (10.211)$$

where λ is a constant which will be chosen to be smaller than k_0.

From the form of $\psi(\xi)$ it can be seen that we consider the particle motion, assuming the $\xi_{\mathbf{k}}$ to be practically equal to zero (compare Skinner's method discussed in Section 6.1). The eigenvalue equation to be satisfied by $\varphi(q,\ \xi^{(0)})$ is of the form

$$(H - T_c)\varphi\psi = E\varphi\psi, \quad (10.212)$$

where the subtraction of T_c corresponds to the adiabatic approximation. If we write

$$U_{\text{eff}} = -\psi^{-1}T_c\psi, \quad (10.213)$$

equation 10.212 can be written in the form

$$(H + U_{eff})\Psi = E\Psi \tag{10.214}$$

and from equations 10.207, 10.208, 10.211, and 6.204 for $\xi_{\mathbf{k}}$ it follows that U_{eff} can be written in the form

$$\left.\begin{array}{l} U_{eff} = \frac{1}{2} \sum_{j \neq n} f(r_{jn}), \\ f(r) = \dfrac{3\hbar^2}{4\pi^2 m\lambda^3} \dfrac{\sin k_0 r - (k_0 r)\cos k_0 r}{(k_0 r)^3}. \end{array}\right\} \tag{10.215}$$

The physical meaning of U_{eff} — called *Zwangspotential* by Brenig — is that it restricts the wave function essentially to those regions of space for which the $\xi_{\mathbf{k}}$ have the chosen values. From equation 10.215 it can be seen that U_{eff} competes with and is large compared to the ordinary potential energy, so that in estimating the energy corresponding to a state with wave function Ψ we can to a first approximation neglect the potential energy.

The energy is given by the equation (compare equation 10.105)

$$E = \frac{\hbar^2}{2m} \frac{\int \sum_j (\boldsymbol{\nabla}_j \varphi^* \cdot \boldsymbol{\nabla}_j \varphi)\, \psi^2\, d^{3N}\mathbf{x}}{\int \varphi^* \varphi\, \psi^2\, d^{3N}\mathbf{x}} \tag{10.216}$$

The ground state corresponds to $\varphi = 1$ (compare the expression of equation 10.206 for $U(k) = 0$, that is, $\lambda_k = 1$), and excited states to $\varphi_{\mathbf{k}} = \sum_j \exp i(\mathbf{k} \cdot \mathbf{x}_j)$ (compare equation 10.102). The presence of the factor ψ excludes the $\mathbf{k}$ belonging to $\{\mathbf{k}\}$, and Brenig shows that for $k > k_0$ equation 10.216 leads to the energy levels

$$E(k) = \hbar^2 k^2/2m^*, \quad m^* = \tfrac{3}{2}\, m.$$

This shows that the excitations for $k > k_0$ correspond to those of a perfect gas of $2N/3$ particles with an effective mass $3m/2$. It may be remarked here that in evaluating the partition function of helium Feynman (1953a) also was led to an effective mass larger than the free mass. Finally we may mention that $\varphi_{\mathbf{k}} \cdot \psi$ is an eigenfunction of the total momentum operator $- i\hbar \sum_j \boldsymbol{\nabla}_j$ with the eigenvalue $\hbar\mathbf{k}$.

Evaluation of the Sums S_k

In chapter 6 we encountered the following sums

$$S_k = \sum_j \exp i(\mathbf{k} \cdot \mathbf{x}_j), \quad \mathbf{k} \neq 0, \tag{A1}$$

where the summation is over all particles in the system. As is clear from the discussion in Chapter 6, it is important to evaluate the average value of S_k and its mean deviation. We shall use Percus and Yevick's analysis (1957a) in this appendix.

First of all we must find the average value $(S_k)_{Av}$ of S_k. Taking a simplistic point of view we can say that one would expect the phase angles $(\mathbf{k} \cdot \mathbf{x}_j)$ to be randomly distributed modulo 2π; this will be the better realized the larger k. We are thus dealing with the sum of N unit vectors in the complex plane which are randomly oriented and we would expect the mean value to be zero. There are now two more problems of interest. The first one is the evaluation of the mean deviation which is now equal to $(|S_k|^2)_{Av}$. The second one is whether it is possible to show that, if at $t = 0$, say, S_k happens to be large, S_k will decrease to its mean value after a certain period.

To answer the first question we can write

$$|S_k|^2 = \sum_{j,n} \exp i(\mathbf{k} \cdot \mathbf{x}_j - \mathbf{x}_n) = N + \sum_{j \neq n} \exp i(\mathbf{k} \cdot \mathbf{x}_j - \mathbf{x}_n), \tag{A2}$$

and we see that the last sum should vanish in the mean for the same reasons as those we used a moment ago to argue that $(S_k)_{Av} = 0$. Alternatively we can consider the absolute magnitude of S_k. If α_k is the phase angle of S_k, we have

$$|S_{\mathbf{k}}| = \sum_j \exp\,[i(\mathbf{k} \cdot \mathbf{x}_j) - i\alpha_{\mathbf{k}}] = \sum_j r_j, \qquad \text{(A3)}$$

where r_j is the real part of $\exp\,[i(\mathbf{k} \cdot \mathbf{x}_j) - i\alpha_{\mathbf{k}}]$. We may expect that for large values of N, $\alpha_{\mathbf{k}}$ will be essentially independent of the $\mathbf{x}_j$, so that the r_j can be considered to be uncorrelated identically correlated random variables. The average value of each r_j is zero and their mean deviation $\frac{1}{2}$. It follows from ordinary probability theory that the probability distribution of $|S_{\mathbf{k}}|$, $w(|S_{\mathbf{k}}|)$, will be given by the equation

$$w(|S_{\mathbf{k}}|) = (N\pi)^{-\frac{1}{2}} \exp\,(-\,|S_{\mathbf{k}}|^2/N), \qquad \text{(A4)}$$

and we see again that $(|S_{\mathbf{k}}|^2)_{\mathrm{Av}} = N$.

To answer the second question we shall assume for the sake of simplicity that we are dealing with noninteracting particles and no external forces. We then have

$$\mathbf{x}_i(t) = \mathbf{x}_i(0) + \mathbf{v}_i t, \qquad \text{(A5)}$$

where the $\mathbf{v}_i$ are constants. To consider an extreme case we shall assume that all products $\mathbf{k} \cdot \mathbf{x}_i(0)$ are equal to zero modulo 2π, so that

$$S_{\mathbf{k}}(0) = N. \qquad \text{(A6)}$$

If $f(\mathbf{v})$ is the normalized probability distribution for the velocities in the system, we get for $S^{\mathbf{k}}(t)$ the equation

$$\begin{aligned} (S_{\mathbf{k}}(t))_{\mathrm{Av}} &= \int \sum_j \exp\,[i(\mathbf{k} \cdot \mathbf{v}_j)t]\{\textstyle\prod_l f(\mathbf{v}_l)\,d^3\,\mathbf{v}_l\} \\ &= N \int \exp\,[i(\mathbf{k} \cdot \mathbf{v})t]f(\mathbf{v})\,d^3\,\mathbf{v}. \end{aligned} \qquad \text{(A7)}$$

We can use for $f(\mathbf{v})$ the Maxwell distribution,

$$f(\mathbf{v}) = (\beta m/2\pi)^{3/2} \exp\,(-\,\tfrac{1}{2}\beta mv^2), \qquad \text{(A8)}$$

where again $\beta = 1/k_{\mathrm{B}}T$ (k_{B} : Boltzmann's constant; T: absolute temperature). The integral in equation A7 can now be evaluated and the result is

$$\big(S_{\mathbf{k}}(t)\big)_{\mathrm{Av}} = \big(S_{\mathbf{k}}(0)\big)_{\mathrm{Av}} \exp\,[-\,k^2 t^2/2\beta m], \qquad \text{(A9)}$$

which shows a rapid decrease to zero, especially for large values of k.

These results would be very satisfactory if it were not for the fact that the $S_{\mathbf{k}}$ are essentially the $\xi_{\mathbf{k}}$ of Section 6.2 which are used to describe collective motion. This means that it is very questionable to assume that the $\mathbf{x}_i$ are sufficiently randomly distributed. In fact they will show correlations corresponding to collective motion and it remains to be shown that also under those circumstances the conclusions of this appendix are valid. It would clearly be of great importance to evaluate $(S_{\mathbf{k}})_{\mathrm{Av}}$ and $(|S_{\mathbf{k}}|^2)_{\mathrm{Av}}$ more rigorously under those circumstances.

The way we have evaluated $(S_{\mathbf{k}})_{\mathrm{Av}}$ here is often called the *random phase approximation*, and for lack of a better approximation we have assumed it to be valid in our discussions.

The Random Phase Approximation

In Chapter 8 we dropped a term in the equations of motion, 8.104, for the case of an electron plasma invoking the random phase approximation (compare also the transition from equation 7.121 to equation 7.122). We shall give here an estimate of the order of magnitude of the term dropped to justify that procedure. We first of all remark that we should expect from the general arguments given in Appendix A that the ratio of the terms R and S, where R and S are given by the equations

$$R = \sum_{j,n,\mathbf{l}(\neq\mathbf{k})} \frac{(\mathbf{l}\cdot\mathbf{k})}{l^2} \exp\left[-i(\mathbf{l}\cdot\mathbf{x}_n)\right] \exp\left[i(\mathbf{l}-\mathbf{k}\cdot\mathbf{x}_j)\right], \quad (B1)$$

$$S = kN^2\xi_\mathbf{k} = N \sum_j \exp\left[-i(\mathbf{k}\cdot\mathbf{x}_j)\right], \quad (B2)$$

will be of the order of $N^{-\frac{1}{2}}$. There remains, however, the question whether or not the coefficient of $N^{-\frac{1}{2}}$ is not too large. The mean value of R is equal to zero, and we are thus interested in its fluctuations. If for a moment we write equation B1 in the form

$$R = k^2 N^2 \sum_{\mathbf{l}(\neq\mathbf{k})} \frac{(\mathbf{l}\cdot\mathbf{k})}{l^2} \xi_\mathbf{l}\xi_{\mathbf{k}-\mathbf{l}}, \quad (B3)$$

and consider equation 8.104 we see that these fluctuations correspond to terms coupling the various collective modes; the neglect of R corresponds thus to a *linearization* of the theory.

In order to evaluate $(R^2)_{Av}$ we follow Pines and Bohm (1952) and split R into two terms, R_1 and R_2, as follows

$$R_1 = \tfrac{1}{2}\sum_{j,n,\mathbf{l}(\neq\mathbf{k})} \frac{k^2}{l^2} \exp\left[-i(\mathbf{l}\cdot\mathbf{x}_n)\right] \exp\left[i(\mathbf{l}-\mathbf{k}\cdot\mathbf{x}_j)\right],$$

$$R_2 = R - R_1. \qquad (B4)$$

It can be shown that R_2 is at most of the same order of magnitude as R_1. To find the order of magnitude of R_1 we write it as follows

$$R_1 = \tfrac{1}{2}k^2\sum_j \exp\left[-i(\mathbf{k}\cdot\mathbf{x}_j)\right]T_\mathbf{l}, \quad T_\mathbf{l} = \sum_\mathbf{l}(N\xi_\mathbf{l}/l)\exp i(\mathbf{l}\cdot\mathbf{x}_j).$$
$$(B5)$$

We now evaluate the average value of $T_\mathbf{l}$ as follows:

$$T_\mathbf{l}^2 = \sum_{\mathbf{l},\mathbf{q}}(N^2\xi_\mathbf{l}\xi_\mathbf{q}/lq)\exp i(\mathbf{l}+\mathbf{q}\cdot\mathbf{x}_j). \qquad (B6)$$

In order to find the average value of $T_\mathbf{l}^2$ we must know the distribution function of the electron gas, preferably in terms of the $\xi_\mathbf{k}$. This function has been evaluated by Pines and Bohm (1952) and using their results we find

$$(T_\mathbf{l}^2)_{\mathrm{Av}} = N\lambda_\mathrm{D}/4\pi. \qquad (B7)$$

Essential in the derivation of equation (B7) is (i) that the distribution function does not depend on the phase of the $\xi_\mathbf{k}$, but only on their absolute magnitude $r_\mathbf{k}$, and (ii) that the distribution function $w(r_\mathbf{k})$ is proportional to $\exp\{-[(4\pi N^2 e^2/k_\mathrm{B}T) + k^2 N^2]r_\mathbf{k}^2\}$. If k is larger than λ_D^{-1}, we get for $(\xi_\mathbf{k}^2)_{\mathrm{Av}}$ the random value $(k^2 N)^{-1}$, but if k is smaller than λ_D^{-1}, the fluctuations are much reduced and are only of the order of λ_D^2/N. This reduction in the fluctuations leads to a convergent expression for $(T_\mathbf{l}^2)_{\mathrm{Av}}$.

From equations B5 and B7 we get

$$(R_1^2)_{\mathrm{Av}} = N^3\lambda_\mathrm{D}k^6\xi_\mathbf{k}^2/16\pi,$$

and for the ratio of this expression to S, using equations B2, 8.106 and 8.107

$$\frac{[(R_1^2)_{\mathrm{Av}}]^{\frac{1}{2}}}{S} = k^2\left(\frac{\lambda_\mathrm{D}}{16\pi N}\right)^{\frac{1}{2}} = \frac{k^2\langle v^2\rangle}{\omega_\mathrm{p}^2}(144\pi\lambda_\mathrm{D}^3 N)^{-\frac{1}{2}}. \qquad (B8)$$

We note first of all the occurrence of the factor $N^{-\frac{1}{2}}$.

Secondly, we note the factor $k^2\langle v^2\rangle/\omega_{\mathrm{p}}^2$ which is always smaller than unity, if k corresponds to a collective mode. Finally we note that if we introduce the mean distance apart, a, of the electrons $(a^3N = 1)$ we can write the last factor in the form $0.05(a/\lambda_{\mathrm{D}})^{3/2}$. As λ_{D} must always be several times larger than a — otherwise there can be no physical significance attached to the Debye length — we see that this factor is always much smaller than unity. The neglect of R, with respect to S, is thus fully justified.

We may add that, if the electron density becomes so large that from equation 8.106 it would follow that $\lambda_{\mathrm{D}} \lesssim a$, we would be in the case where degenerate Fermi statistics should be used and these will themselves severely reduce the fluctuations (see, for instance, ter Haar 1954, Ch. 7) due to the operation of the exclusion principle.

Derivation of the Effective Mass Equation

In this appendix we want to describe briefly Kohn's derivation of the Hamiltonian of equation 5.120 and to show how Kohn's method also leads approximately to the wave function of equation 5.122. For details we refer to Kohn's paper (1957). The situation treated by Kohn is the following one. Consider an insulator with N electrons in the system and charges $Z_l e$ on the nuclei which are supposed to be fixed at $\mathbf{X}_l$, and let us add to this system one extra electron, which in the ground state will occupy the lowest energy level of the conduction band. The Hamiltonian $H^{(0)}$ of the system is given by equation 5.102

$$H^{(0)} = -\frac{\hbar^2}{2m} \sum_j \nabla_j{}^2 - \sum_{j,l} \frac{Z_l e^2}{|\mathbf{x}_j - \mathbf{X}_l|} + \tfrac{1}{2}\sum_{j \neq n} \frac{e^2}{r_{jn}}, \quad (C1)$$

where the summation over l is over all nuclei, where the $\mathbf{x}_j$ are the position coordinates of the electrons, where $r_{jn} = |\mathbf{x}_j - \mathbf{x}_n|$, and where j and n run from 1 to $N + 1$. Let $\Psi_{n,\mathbf{k}}$ be the normalized eigenfunctions of $H^{(0)}$ of the form

$$\Psi_{n,\mathbf{k}} = \exp i(\mathbf{k} \cdot \mathbf{x}_1)\Phi_{n,\mathbf{k}}, \quad (C2)$$

where $\mathbf{x}_1$ is the coordinate of the last electron and where $\Phi_{n,\mathbf{k}}$ is a function with the same periodicity as the lattice. The corresponding eigenvalue will be denoted by $E_{n,\mathbf{k}}$. We shall assume that the lowest energy state corresponds to $\mathbf{k} = 0$ and we shall denote the corresponding quantum number n by 0. As we are dealing with an insulator, $E_{n,0}$ will always be larger than $E_{0,0}$ by a finite amount. For small values of $k(= |\mathbf{k}|)$ we can write in the case of cubic symmetry

$$E_{0,\mathbf{k}} \rightleftharpoons E_{0,0} + \tfrac{1}{2}ak^2 = E_{0,0} + \hbar^2 k^2/2m_0, \qquad (C3)$$

where the last equation follows from the usual definition in the case of the one-electron picture and at the moment is used to define the effective mass m_0. Kohn claims that this mass m_0 is, indeed, the mass measured by a cyclotron-resonance experiment.

Consider now the case where the $N + 1$ electron was produced by a donor atom, that is, a nucleus with a charge $(Z_l + 1)e$ which we shall assume to be situated at the origin. This will lead to a Hamiltonian H given by the equation

$$H = H^{(0)} + H^{(1)}, \qquad H^{(1)} = -\sum_j \frac{e^2}{r_j}\left(+\sum \frac{Z_l e^2}{|\mathbf{X}_l|}\right). \qquad (C4)$$

We shall use perturbation theory to find the eigenfunctions Ψ of H. We expand Ψ in terms of the $\Psi_{n,\mathbf{k}}$,

$$\Psi = \sum_{\mathbf{k}} A_{\mathbf{k}} \Psi_{0,\mathbf{k}} + \sum_{n \neq 0, \mathbf{k}} A_{n,\mathbf{k}} \Psi_{n,\mathbf{k}}. \qquad (C5)$$

As we are interested in the states in the neighbourhood of the ground state we expect that only those $A_{\mathbf{k}}$ and $A_{n,\mathbf{k}}$ will appreciably differ from zero for which $kd \ll 1$ (d: lattice parameter). Moreover, as $E_{n,0} - E_{0,0}$ will in that case be large compared to $E_{0,\mathbf{k}} - E_{0,0}$ it can be shown that the sum for $n \neq 0$ can be neglected.

From the usual equations of perturbation theory (for instance, Kramers 1957, § 48) we get for the $A_{\mathbf{k}}$ the equations

$$(E_{0,\mathbf{k}}-E)A_{\mathbf{k}} + \sum_{\mathbf{k}'} H^{(1)}_{\mathbf{k}\mathbf{k}'} A_{\mathbf{k}'} = 0, \quad H^{(1)}_{\mathbf{k}\mathbf{k}'} = \int \Psi^*_{0,\mathbf{k}} H_1 \Psi_{0,\mathbf{k}'} d^{3N+3}\mathbf{x}. \qquad (C6)$$

We must now evaluate the matrix elements $H^{(1)}_{\mathbf{k}\mathbf{k}'}$ Kohn shows that the diagonal elements do not depend on $\mathbf{k}$, while for the off-diagonal elements we have

$$H^{(1)}_{\mathbf{k}\mathbf{k}'} = -e^2 \int f(\mathbf{k},\ \mathbf{k}';\ \mathbf{x}_1) \exp\left[i(\mathbf{x}_1 \cdot \mathbf{k} - \mathbf{k}')\right] \frac{d^3\mathbf{x}_1}{|\mathbf{x}_1|}, (C7)$$

where

$$f(\mathbf{k}, \mathbf{k}'; \mathbf{x}_1) = (N + 1) \int \Phi_{0,\mathbf{k}}^{*} \Phi_{0,\mathbf{k}'} d^{3N} \mathbf{x}. \qquad \text{(C8)}$$

In equation C8 the integration is over all coordinates, but $\mathbf{x}_1$, and the factor $N + 1$ derives from the sum over j in equation C4. To a first approximation the dependence of $f(\mathbf{k}, \mathbf{k}')$ on $\mathbf{x}_1$ can be neglected (this can be seen by expanding it in a Fourier series in which the exponents involve the scalar product of $\mathbf{x}_1$ and lattice vectors, evaluating the integral in equation C7, and bearing in mind the fact that kd and $k'd$ will be small compared to one). We can now evaluate $H_{\mathbf{k}\mathbf{k}'}^{(1)}$, and the result is

$$H_{\mathbf{k}\mathbf{k}'}^{(1)} = -\frac{4\pi e^2}{\varepsilon |\mathbf{k}' - \mathbf{k}|^2}, \quad \mathbf{k}' \neq \mathbf{k}, \qquad \text{(C9)}$$

where ε is given by the equation

$$\varepsilon = \lim_{k \to 0,\, k' \to 0,\, \mathbf{k}' \neq \mathbf{k}} f(\mathbf{k}, \mathbf{k}'; \mathbf{x}_1). \qquad \text{(C10)}$$

It can be shown (see Kohn 1957) that ε is in fact the static dielectric constant of the medium (we are again assuming the system to be in a unit volume). Substituting into equation C6, using equation C3, and putting

$$E' = E - E_{0,0} - H_{\mathbf{k}\mathbf{k}}^{(1)}, \qquad \text{(C11)}$$

we have finally

$$\left[\frac{\hbar^2 k^2}{2m_0} - E' \right] A_{\mathbf{k}} - \frac{4\pi e^2}{\varepsilon} \sum_{\mathbf{k}'} \frac{A_{\mathbf{k}'}}{|\mathbf{k}' - \mathbf{k}|^2} = 0. \qquad \text{(C12)}$$

We can now introduce a function $\chi'(\mathbf{x})$ by the equation

$$\chi'(\mathbf{x}) = \sum_{\mathbf{k}} A_{\mathbf{k}} \exp i(\mathbf{k} \cdot \mathbf{x}), \qquad \text{(C13)}$$

and we find for χ' the "Schrödinger" equation

$$\left[-\frac{\hbar^2}{2m_0} \nabla^2 - \frac{e^2}{\varepsilon |\mathbf{x}|} - E' \right] \chi' = 0, \qquad \text{(C14)}$$

which concludes the derivation of equation 5.120.

To see that Ψ of equation C5 is approximately the same as the one-electron wave function of equation 5.122, we note first of all that to a first approximation we may assume $\Phi_{0,\mathbf{k}}$ to be the product of a Bloch function (see equation 5.104) for the last electron and a Slater determinant D for the other electrons

$$\Psi_{0,\mathbf{k}} \rightleftharpoons \exp i(\mathbf{k} \cdot \mathbf{x}) \, u_{\mathbf{k}}(\mathbf{x})D. \tag{C15}$$

We may also assume that for states near the ground state D will not appreciably depend on $\mathbf{k}$. Neglecting as before in equation C5 all terms with $n \neq 0$, we get for Ψ the expression

$$\Psi \rightleftharpoons D \sum_{\mathbf{k}} A_{\mathbf{k}} \exp i(\mathbf{k} \cdot \mathbf{x}) u_{\mathbf{k}}(\mathbf{x}). \tag{C16}$$

We mentioned in connexion with equation 5.108 that $u_{\mathbf{k}}(\mathbf{x})$ will depend only very slightly on $\mathbf{k}$ so that to a further approximation we can write

$$\Psi \rightleftharpoons Du_0(\mathbf{x}) \sum_{\mathbf{k}} A_{\mathbf{k}} \exp i(\mathbf{k} \cdot \mathbf{x}) = Du_0(\mathbf{x}) \chi'(\mathbf{x}), \tag{C17}$$

where we have used the definition of equation C13 of χ'. As $\mathbf{k} = 0$ corresponds to the band edge wave vector, we see that apart from the extra factor D which involves the behaviour of all the other electrons, we are back to equation 5.122 with χ' satisfying equation C14. In the case of a donor atom, the perturbing potential U_1 is, however, given by the equation

$$U_1 = - e^2/\varepsilon r, \tag{C18}$$

and we see that, indeed, equation C14 is a special case of equation 5.123.

References

Adams, E. N., 1955, *Phys. Rev.* **98**, 1130.
Ahiezer, A., 1956, *Nuovo cimento* **3**, *Suppl.*, 591.
Allcock, G. R., 1956, *Advances in Phys.* **5**, 412.
Allcock, G. R., and C. G. Kuper, 1955, *Proc. Roy. Soc. (London)* **A231**, 226.
Anselm, A. I., and Iu. A. Firsov, 1955, *JETP (U.S.S.R.)* **28**, 151, *JETP (U.S.S.R.)* **1**, 139, 1955).
Bardeen, J., and D. Pines, 1955, *Phys. Rev.* **99**, 1140.
Barrie, R., 1956, *Phys. Rev.* **103**, 1581.
Bassani, F., and N. Inchauspé, 1957, *Phys. Rev.* **105**, 819.
Berz, F., 1956, *Proc. Phys. Soc. (London)* **B69**, 939.
Bethe, H. A., 1937, *Revs. Modern Phys.* **9**, 69; 1956, *Phys. Rev.* **103**, 1353.
Blatt, F. J., 1955, *Phys. Rev.* **99**, 1735.
Bloch, F., 1928, *Z. Physik* **52**, 555; 1930, *Z. Physik* **61**, 206.
Boer, J. de, 1949, *Repts. Progr. in Phys.* **12**, 305.
Bogoliubov, N. N., and D. N. Zubarev, 1955, *JETP (U.S.S.R.)* **28**, 129 (1955, *JETP (U.S.S.R.)* **1**, 83).
Bohm, D., and E. P. Gross, 1949, *Phys. Rev.* **75**, 1851.
Bohm, D., K. Huang, and D. Pines, 1957, *Phys. Rev.* **107**, 71.
Bohm, D., and D. Pines, 1951, *Phys. Rev.* **82**, 625; 1953, *Phys. Rev.* **92**, 609.
Bohr, A., 1952, *Proc. Danish Acad. Sci.* **26**, No. 14; 1954, *Rotational States of Atomic Nuclei*, Munksgaard, Copenhagen.
Bohr, A., and B. R. Mottelson, 1953, *Proc. Danish Acad. Sci.* **27**, No. 16.
Bohr, N., 1936a, b, *Nature* **137**, 344, 351.
Bohr, N., and F. Kalckar, 1937, *Proc. Danish Acad. Sci.* **14**, No. 10.
Bohr, N., and J. A. Wheeler, 1939, *Phys. Rev.* **56**, 426.
Bontsch-Brujewitsch, W. L., 1955, *Uspekhi Fiz. Nauk* **56**, 55 (1955, *Fortschr. Physik* **3**, 371).
Born, M., and T. von Kármán, 1912, *Physik. Z.* **13**, 297; 1913, *Physik. Z.* **14**, 15.
Brenig, W., 1956, *Z. Physik* **144**, 488; 1957, *Nuclear Phys.* **4**, 363.
Brueckner, K. A., 1954, *Phys. Rev.* **96**, 508; 1955a, *Phys. Rev.* **97**, 1353; 1955b, *Phys. Rev.* **100**, 36.
Brueckner, K. A., R. J. Eden, and N. C. Francis, 1955, *Phys. Rev.* **99**, 76.
Brueckner, K. A., and C. A. Levinson, 1955, *Phys. Rev.* **97**, 1344.
Brueckner, K. A., C. A. Levinson, and H. M. Mahmoud, 1954, *Phys. Rev.* **95**, 217.
Brueckner, K. A., and K. Sawada, 1957a, b, *Phys. Rev.* **106**, 1117, 1128.

Bijl, A., 1940, *Physica* 7, 869.
Chalatnikow, I. M., 1956a, *Uspekhi Fiz. Nauk* 59, 673 (1957, *Fortschr. Physik* 5, 211); 1956b, *Uspekhi Fiz. Nauk* 60, 69 (1957, *Fortschr. Physik* 5, 287).
Chester, G. V., 1954a, *Phys. Rev.* 93, 1412; 1954b, *Phys. Rev.* 94, 246.
Chew, G. F., and M. L. Goldberger, 1952, *Phys. Rev.* 87, 778.
Clemmow, P. C., and A. J. Willson, 1956, *Proc. Roy. Soc. (London)* A237, 117.
Coester, F., 1955, *Phys. Rev.* 99, 170.
Corson, E. M., 1951, *Perturbation Methods in the Quantum Mechanics of n-Electron Systems*, Blackie & Son, Glasgow.
Debye, P., 1912, *Ann. Physik* 39, 789.
Debye, P., and E. Hückel, 1923, *Physik. Z.* 24, 185.
Dekker, A. J., 1957, *Solid State Physics*, Prentice Hall, Englewood Cliffs, N. J.
Diemer, G., and W. Hoogenstraaten, 1957, *Phys. and Chem. Solids* 2, 119.
Dingle, R. B., 1955, *Phil. Mag.* 46, 831.
Dirac, P. A. M., 1930, *Proc. Cambridge Phil. Soc.* 26, 376.
Dresselhaus, G., 1956, *Phys. and Chem. Solids* 1, 15.
Dresselhaus, G., A. F. Kip, and C. Kittel, 1955, *Phys. Rev.* 100, 618.
Dyson, F. J., 1957, *Phys. Rev.* 106, 20.
Ecker, G., 1955a, b, Z. *Physik* 140, 274, 293; 1955c, Z. *Physik* 141, 294; 1955d, *Appl. Sci. Research* B5, 321.
Eden, R. J., 1956, *Proc. Roy. Soc. (London)* A235, 408; 1958, Chapter in *Nuclear Reactions*, North-Holland Pub. Co., Amsterdam.
Eden, R. J., and N. C. Francis, 1955, *Phys. Rev.* 97, 1366.
Ehrenfest, P., 1927, Z. *Physik* 45, 455.
Einstein, A., 1925, *Berliner Ber.* 1925, 3.
Fano, U., 1956, *Phys. Rev.* 103, 1202.
Fényes, I., 1948, Z. *Physik* 125, 336.
Ferentz, M., M. Gell-Mann, and D. Pines, 1953, *Phys. Rev* 92, 836.
Fermi, E., 1928, Z. *Physik* 48, 73.
Ferrell, R. A., 1956, *Phys. Rev.* 101, 554; 1957, *Phys. Rev.* 107, 450.
Ferrell, R. A., and J. J. Quinn, 1957, *Phys. Rev.* 108, 570.
Feshbach, H., C. E. Porter, and V. F. Weisskopf, 1955, *Phys. Rev.* 98, 783.
Feynman, R. P., 1953a, b, *Phys. Rev.* 91, 1291, 1301; 1954, *Phys. Rev.* 94, 262; 1955, *Progr. in Low Temp. Phys.* 1, 17; 1955a, *Phys. Rev.* 97, 660.
Feynman, R. P., and M. Cohen, 1956, *Phys. Rev.* 102, 1189.
Fock, V., 1930, Z. *Physik* 61, 126.
Fowler, R. H., and H. Jones, 1938, *Proc. Cambridge Phil. Soc.* 34, 573.
Frenkel, J., 1928, Z. *Physik* 50, 234; 1931a, b, *Phys. Rev.* 37, 17, 1276.
Friedel, J., 1954, *Advances in Phys.* 3, 446.
Fröhlich, H., 1954, *Advances in Phys.* 3, 325.
Fröhlich, H., and S. Doniach, 1956, *Proc. Phys. Soc. (London)* B69, 661.
Fujita, J., 1956, *Progr. Theoret. Phys. (Kyoto)* 16, 112.

Gabor, D., 1952, *Proc. Roy. Soc. (London)* **A213**, 73.
Galasiewicz, Z., 1955, *Acta Phys. Polon.* **14**, 373; 1956a, b, *Acta Phys. Polon* **15**, 49, 79.
Gáspár, R., 1952a, *J. Chem. Phys.* **20**, 1863; 1952b, *Acta Phys. Acad. Sci. Hung.* **2**, 151; 1954, *Acta Phys. Acad. Sci. Hung.* **3**, 263.
Gell-Mann, M., 1957, *Phys. Rev.* **106**, 369.
Gell-Mann, M., and K. A. Brueckner, 1957, *Phys. Rev.* **106**, 364.
Goldhaber, M., and E. Teller, 1948, *Phys. Rev.* **74**, 1046.
Goldstein, H., 1950, *Classical Mechanics*, Addison-Wesley, Cambridge, Mass.
Goldstein, L., and J. Reekie, 1955, *Phys. Rev.* **98**, 857.
Goldstone, J., 1957, *Proc. Roy. Soc. (London)* **A239**, 267.
Gombás, P., 1949, *Die statistische Theorie des Atoms*, Springer, Vienna; 1956, *Handb. Phys.* **36**, 109; 1957, *Fortschr. Physik* **5**, 1.
Gombás, P., and K. Ladányi, 1955, *Acta Phys. Acad. Sci. Hung.* **5**, 313.
Green, H. S., 1952, *A Molecular Theory of Fluids*, North-Holland Pub. Co., Amsterdam.
Groschwitz, E., and K. Siebertz, 1956, *Z. Naturforsch.* **11a**, 482.
Gross, E. F., and M. A. Jacobson, 1955, *Doklady Akad. Nauk S.S.S.R.* **102**, 485.
Gross, E. F., and A. A. Kaplianskii, 1955, *J. Tech. Phys. (U.S.S.R.)* **25**, 2061.
Gross, E. F., A. A. Kaplianskii, and B. V. Novikov, 1956, *Doklady Akad. Nauk S.S.S.R.* **110**, 761 (1957, *Soviet Phys. Doklady* **1**, 582).
Gross, E. F., B. P. Zakharchenia, and N. M. Reinov, 1954, *Doklady Akad. Nauk. S.S.S.R.* **99**, 527; 1956, *J. Tech. Phys. (U.S.S.R.)* **26**, 700 (1957, *Soviet Phys. Tech. Phys.* **1**, 677).
Haar, D. ter, 1949, *Phys. Rev.* **76**, 1525; 1954, *Elements of Statistical Mechanics*, Rinehart, New York; 1954a, *Phys. Rev.* **95**, 895; 1957, *Repts. Prog. in Phys.* **20**, 130; 1957a, see Prigogine, 1958.
Haken, H., 1953, *Z. Physik* **135**, 408; 1954a, *Halbleiterprobleme*, **1**, 70: 1954b, *Z. Physik* **139**, 66; 1955a, *Halbleiterprobleme* 2, 1; 1955b, *Z. Naturforsch.* **10a**, 253; 1956a, b, *Z. Physik* **146**, 527, 555; 1956c, *Z. Naturforsch.* **11a**, 875; 1956d, *Nuovo cimento* **3**, 1230; 1956e, *Nuovo cimento* **4**, 1608; 1957, *Z. Physik* **147**, 323; 1958, *Fortschr. Physik* (in press).
Hartree, D. R., 1928, *Proc. Cambridge Phil. Soc.* **24**, 89; 1948, *Repts. Progr. in Phys.* **11**, 113.
Heisenberg, W., 1931, *Ann. physik* **10**, 888.
Hill, D. L., and J. A. Wheeler, 1953, *Phys. Rev.* **89**, 1102.
Hirschfelder, J. O., C. F. Curtiss, and R. B. Bird, 1954, *Molecular Theory of Gases and Liquids*, Wiley, New York.
Höhler, G., 1955a, *Z. Physik* **140**, 192; 1955b, *Nuovo cimento* **2**, 691; 1956a, b, *Z. Physik* **146**, 372, 571.
Hrivnák, L., 1957, *Czechoslov. J. Phys.* **7**, 395.
Huang, K., and C. N. Yang, 1957, *Phys. Rev.* **105**, 767.
Huang, K., C. N. Yang, and J. M. Luttinger, 1957, *Phys. Rev.* **105**, 776.

Hubbard, J., 1954, *Proc. Phys. Soc.* (*London*) **A67**, 1058; 1955a, b, *Proc. Phys. Soc.* (*London*) **A68**, 441, 976; 1957a, *Proc. Roy. Soc.* (*London*) **A240**, 539; 1957b, *Proc. Roy. Soc.* (*London*) A, (in press).

Hund, F., 1956, *Handb. Phys.*, **36**, 1.

James, H. M., 1949a, b. *Phys. Rev.* **76**. 1602, 1611.

Jancovici, B., 1957, *Phys. Rev.* **107**, 631.

Jastrow, R., 1955, *Phys. Rev.* **98**, 1478.

Jull, G. W., 1956, *Proc. Phys. Soc.* (*London*) **B69**, 1237.

Kampen, N. G. van, 1955, *Physica* **21**, 949; 1957, *Physica* **23**, 641.

Kanazawa, H., 1955, *Progr. Theoret. Phys.* (*Kyoto*) **13**, 227; 1956a, *Progr. Theoret. Phys.* (*Kyoto*) **15**, 273; 1956b, *Sci. Papers Coll. Gen. Educ. Univ. Tokyo* **6**, 23; 1957, *Progr. Theoret. Phys.* (*Kyoto*) **17**, 1.

Keesom, W. H., 1942, *Helium*, Elsevier Pub. Co., Amsterdam, Ch. VIII.

Kinoshita, T., and Y. Nambu, 1954, *Phys. Rev.* **94**, 598.

Kirkwood, J. G., 1946, *J. Chem. Phys.* **14**, 180.

Kisslinger, L. S., 1956, *Phys. Rev.* **104**, 1077.

Kittel, C., 1954, *Am. J. Phys.* **22**, 250.

Kohn, W., 1957, *Phys. Rev.* **105**, 509.

Kramers, H. A., 1935, *Physica* **2**, 483; 1938, *Nuovo cimento* **15**, 108; 1947, *Physica* **13**, 401; 1957, *Quantum Mechanics*, North-Holland Publ. Co., Amsterdam.

Kromhout, R. A., 1957, *Phys. Rev.* **107**, 215.

Kronig, R., and J. Korringa, 1943, *Physica* **10**, 406.

Kronig, R., and A. Thellung 1952, *Physica* **18**, 749.

Kümmel, H., 1957a, *Z. Naturforsch.* 12a, 85; 1957b, *Nuovo cimento.* (in press).

Kuper, C. G., 1956, *Proc. Phys. Soc.* (*London*) **A69**, 492.

Lamb, W. E., and R. C. Retherford, 1947, *Phys. Rev.* **72**, 241.

Lampert, M. A., 1956, *J. Appl. Phys.* **27**, 5.

Landau, L., 1941, *J. Phys.* (*U.S.S.R.*) **5**, 71; 1946, *J. Phys.* (*U.S.S.R.*) **10**, 25; 1947, *J. Phys.* (*U.S.S.R.*) **11**, 91.

Lang, W., 1948, *Optik* **3**, 233.

Lee, T. D., K. Huang, and C. N. Yang, 1957, *Phys. Rev.* **106**, 1135.

Lenz, W., 1932, *Z. Physik* **77**, 713.

Lindhard, J., 1954, *Proc. Danish Acad. Sci.* **28**, No. 8.

Lipkin, H. J., A. de Shalit, and I. Talmi, 1955, *Nuovo cimento* **2**, 773.

Löwdin, P. O., 1955a, b, c, *Phys. Rev.* **97**, 1474, 1490, 1509; 1956, *Advances in Phys.* **5**, 1.

London, F., 1938, *Phys. Rev.* **54**, 947.

Lorentz, H. A., 1909, *The Theory of Electrons*, Teubner, Leipzig.

Mansfield, R., 1956, *Proc. Phys. Soc.* (*London*) **B69**, 76.

March, N. H., 1957, *Advances in Phys.* **6**, 1.

Margenau, H., 1931a, *Phys. Rev.* **37**, 1425; 1931b, *Phys. Rev.* **38**, 747; 1939, *Phys. Rev.* **56**, 1000.

Martienssen, W., 1957, *Phys. and Chem. Solids* **2**, 257.

Marton, L., L. B. Leder, and H. Mendlowitz, 1955, *Advances in Electronics and Electron Phys.* 7, 183.

Mayer, M. G., 1948, *Phys. Rev.* 74, 235.

Meyer, H. J. G., 1956a, *Physica* 22, 109; 1956b, Amsterdam thesis.

Miyazima, T., and T. Tamura, 1956, *Progr. Theoret. Phys. (Kyoto)* 15, 255.

Morse, P. M., 1936, *Vibration and Sound*, McGraw-Hill, New York.

Muto, T., and H. Okuno, 1956, *J. Phys. Soc. Japan* 11, 633; 1957, *J. Phys. Soc. Japan* 12, 108.

Neumann, J. von, 1955, *Mathematical Foundations of Quantum Mechanics*, Princeton Univ. Press, Princeton, N. J.

Nikitine, S., 1955, *Helv. Phys. Acta* 28, 308; 1956, *J. Phys. radium* 17, 817.

Nikitine, S., G. Perny, and M. Sieskind, *Compt. rend.* 238, 67.

Nikitine, S., R. Reiss, and G. Perny, *Compt. Rend.* 242, 2540.

Nishiyama, T., 1951, *Progr. Theoret. Phys. (Kyoto)* 6, 366; 1954, *Progr. Theoret. Phys. (Kyoto)* 12, 265; 1955, *Progr. Theoret. Phys. (Kyoto)* 14, 37; 1956, *Progr. Theoret. Phys. (Kyoto)* 16, 244.

Peierls, R. E., 1932, *Ann. Physik* 13, 905; 1955, *The Quantum Theory of Solids*, Oxford, New York.

Pekar, S. I., 1946, *JETP (U.S.S.R.)* 16, 341; 1953, *Uspekhi Fiz. Nauk* 50, 197 (1954, *Fortschr. Physik* 1, 367); *Untersuchungen über die Elektronentheorie der Kristalle*, Akademie Verlag, Berlin; 1956, *Fortschr. Physik* 4, 383.

Penrose, O., 1954, *Phil. Mag.* 45, 80.

Percus, J. K., and G. J. Yevick, 1956, *Phys. Rev.* 101, 1192; 1957a, b, *Nuovo cimento* 5, 65, 1057; 1957c, *Phys. Rev.*; 1957d, *Nuovo cimento*; 1957e, *Phys. Rev.* (in press).

Pfirsch, D., and E. Spenke, 1954, *Z. Physik* 137, 309.

Pines, D., 1953, *Phys. Rev.* 92, 626; 1954, *Proc. Solvay Congress*; 1955, *Solid State Phys.* 1, 367; 1956, *Revs. Modern Physics* 28, 184.

Pines, D., and D. Bohm, 1952, *Phys. Rev.* 85, 338.

Pomerantschuk, I. J., 1941a, b, *JETP (U.S.S.R.)* 11, 226, 246.

Pomerantschuk, I. J., and A. I. Ahiezer, 1944, *JETP (U.S.S.R.)* 14, 342.

Prigogine, I., ed., *Proceedings of the International Symposium on Transport Processes in Statistical Mechanics*, Interscience, New York, 1958.

Raimes, S., 1956, *Research (London)* 9, 374; 1957, *Repts. Progr. in Phys.* 20, 1.

Rainwater, J., 1950, *Phys. Rev.* 79, 432.

Reekie, J., and T. S. Hutchison, 1953, *Phys. Rev.* 92, 827.

Rosen, N., 1931, *Phys. Rev.* 38, 255.

Rosen, P., 1950, *J. Chem. Phys.* 18, 1182.

Ruthemann, G., 1951, *Naturwissenschaften* 29, 648; 1942, *Naturwissenschaften* 30, 145; 1948, *Ann. Physik* 2, 113.

Sawada, K., 1957, *Phys. Rev.* 106, 372.

Schiff, L. I., 1949, *Quantum Mechanics*, McGraw-Hill, New York.

Schultz, T. D., 1956, *Mass. Inst. Technol. Solid State and Molecular Theory Group, Tech. Rept.* No. 9 (unpublished).

Seitz, F., 1940, *The Modern Theory of Solids*, McGraw-Hill, New York; 1954, *Revs. Modern Phys.* **26**, 7.

Seraphin, B., 1955, *Halbleiterprobleme* **2**, 40.

Skinner, R., 1956, *Can. J. Phys.* **34**, 901.

Skyrme, T. H. R., 1956, *Phil. Mag.* **1**, 1043; 1957, *Proc. Roy. Soc. (London)* **A239**, 399; 1957a, *Proc. Phys. Soc. (London)* **A70**, 433.

Slater, J. C., 1928, *Phys. Rev.* **32**, 349; 1929, *Phys. Rev.* **34**, 1293; 1949, *Phys. Rev.* **76**, 1592; 1954, *Mass. Inst. Technol. Solid State and Molecular Theory Group*, *Tech. Rept.* No. 6 (unpublished).

Slater, J. C., and J. G. Kirkwood, 1931, *Phys. Rev.* **37**, 682.

Sommerfeld, A., 1928, *Z. Physik* **47**, 1.

Sommerfeld, A., and H. Bethe, 1933, *Handb. Phys.* **24₂**, 333.

Steenbeck, M., 1932, *Z. Physik* **76**, 260.

Süssmann, G., 1954, *Z. Physik* **139**, 543.

Tamura, T., 1956, *Nuovo cimento* **4**, 713.

Thellung, A., 1953, *Physica* **19**, 217; 1956, *Helv. Phys. Acta* **29**, 103.

Thomas, L. H., 1927, *Proc. Cambridge Phil. Soc.* **23**, 542.

Tiablikov, S. V., 1953, *JETP (U.S.S.R.)* **25**, 688.

Tobocman, W., 1957, *Phys. Rev.* **107**, 203.

Tolhoek, H. A., 1954, *Ned. Tijdschr. Natuurk.* **20**, 259; 1955, *Physica* **21**, 1.

Tomonaga, S., 1950, *Progr. Theoret. Phys. (Kyoto)* **5**, 544; 1955a, b, *Progr. Theoret. Phys. (Kyoto)* **13**, 467, 482.

Tonks, L., and I. Langmuir, 1929, *Phys. Rev.* **33**, 195.

Trlifaj, M., 1956, *Czechoslov. J. Phys.* **6**, 533; 1957, *Czechoslov. J. Phys.* **7**, 379.

Twiss, R. Q., 1952, *Phys. Rev.* **88**, 1392.

Vlasov, A., 1945, *J. Phys. (U.S.S.R.)* **9**, 25.

Wageningen, R. van, and J. de Boer, 1952, *Physica* **18**, 369.

Wannier, G. H., 1937, *Phys. Rev.* **52**, 191.

Watanabe, Y., 1956, *Progr. Theoret. Phys. (Kyoto)* **16**, 534.

Weisskopf, V. F., 1951, *Science* **113**, 101.

Weizsäcker, C. F. von, 1935, *Z. Physik* **96**, 431.

Wergeland, H., 1945, *Fysik. Verden, Fra* **1945**, 223.

Wigner, E., 1934, *Phys. Rev.* **46**, 1002; 1938, *Trans. Faraday Soc.* **34**, 678.

Wigner, E., and F. Seitz, 1933, *Phys. Rev.* **43**, 804; 1934, *Phys. Rev.* **46**, 509.

Wilks, J., 1957, *Repts. Progr. Phys.* **20**, 38.

Wilson, A. H., 1953, *Theory of Metals*, Cambridge, New York.

Wolff, P. A., 1953, *Phys. Rev.* **92**, 18.

Wonssowski, S. W., 1952, *Uspekhi Fiz. Nauk* **48**, 289 (*Fortschr. Physik* **1**, 239, 1954).

Yang, C. N., and T. D. Lee, 1952, *Phys. Rev.* **87**, 404.

Yevick, G. J., and J. K. Percus, 1956, *Phys. Rev.* **101**, 1186.

Yvon, J., 1934, *Actualités sci. et ind.* No. **203**.

Ziman, J. M., 1953, *Proc. Roy. Soc. (London)* **A219**, 257.

Zubarev, D. N., 1953, *JETP (U.S.S.R.)* **25**, 548; 1954, *Doklady Akad. Nauk S.S.S.R.* **95**, 757; 1955, *JETP (U.S.S.R.)* **29**, 881 (1956), *JETP (U.S.S.R.)* **2**, 745.

Index